CHILDREN AS WRITERS

Award-winning entries from the
15th Daily Mirror Children's
Literary Competition

Children as Writers

*Award-winning entries from the
15th Daily Mirror Children's
Literary Competition*

HEINEMANN
LONDON

Heinemann Educational Books

LONDON EDINBURGH MELBOURNE AUCKLAND
TORONTO HONG KONG SINGAPORE KUALA LUMPUR
IBADAN NAIROBI JOHANNESBURG
NEW DELHI LUSAKA

ISBN 0 435 13400 0 (Cased)
 0 435 13401 9 (Paperback)

Published by
Heinemann Educational Books Ltd
48 Charles Street, London W1X 8AH
Printed in Great Britain by
Butler & Tanner Ltd, Frome and London

Foreword

We had a very large number of admirable entries from young writers of all ages from 6 to 16 and, as in previous years, the Preliminary Selection Committee and the Advisory Panel have both been hard put to choose the best. We wish we could have printed more, since often the distinction between what was chosen and what was omitted was a fine one, and, if our verdicts were often unanimous, they were still necessarily subjective.

That is one of the reasons why I hope that many of those who have learnt to write honestly about the things that they want to write about will go on doing so, whether they have won prizes or mentions in this competition or not. Our civilisation is short on communication, and long on prejudice and incomprehension, so we have great need of them, the genuine communicators.

If some of the ideas and values, which the authors of what is here printed express, seem strange or disturbing to readers who are long past the age of 16, we may do well to remember that most human advance results from the tension between the traditional and the startling. It is very much to the credit of the *Daily Mirror* that the numerous readers of this fifteenth edition of *Children as Writers* will have the chance of discovering, to their profit, the best of what their children are trying to say to them.

JACK LONGLAND

Introduction

Year by year the Children's Literary Competition organised by the *Daily Mirror* attracts work of remarkable quality and extraordinary range from Britain's boys and girls.

More than 55,000 pieces of poetry, prose and drama were submitted for our 15th contest and once again the judges were faced with the task of choosing the award winners from a wealth of talent.

This latest edition of *Children as Writers* presents in permanent form the best from the rich and varied volume of work sent in for that 1973 competition.

Many people help in the organisation of our contest and sincere thanks are extended to them for their very real interest and involvement.

It gives us all at the *Daily Mirror* much pleasure that our competition provides budding poets, authors and playwrights with such a stimulating outlet for self-expression. The fact that some of our award winners have pursued their writing to win further success in the literary world has been especially gratifying.

ANTHONY MILES
Editor, Daily Mirror

Contents

Eight years and under

the blue whale   1
Martin Robert Vanner
Bluehouse Infant School
Basildon
Essex

Who Is It*   4
Rachel Howe
Carterknowle Junior School
Sheffield
South Yorkshire

The Adventures of Tiny Tim Mouse   6
Paul Stephen Barned
Joydens Wood Junior School
Wilmington
Kent

The Deep Pond   7
Michele Hutchinson
Deanwood County Junior School
Gillingham
Kent

The Skull*   8
Martin Miles Baul
Bishop Thornton C.E. School
Ripley
Harrogate
North Yorkshire

* Award winner

The Serpent 8
Shaun Matthew Chaplin
The Junior School
St Lawrence College
Ramsgate
Kent

My Muddly Bed 8
Sally Lynn Clark
Catherine de Barnes C.E. Primary School
Solihull
West Midlands

The Sky at Night* 9
Helen Louise Garrick
Westpark First School
Newcastle-upon-Tyne

I'll Finish It* 9
Saira Elizabeth Shah
Langton House School
Langton Green
Kent

The River 10
Hazel Crane
Woodstock C.E. Primary School
Woodstock
Oxfordshire

In the Beginning* 10
Alan Paterson Dixon
Normand Park Junior School
London SW6

Sounds 11
Julie Kelford
Normand Park Junior School
London SW6

The Flood* 11
Hilary Teresa Sheppard
Swithun Wells R.C. School
Chandler's Ford
Eastleigh
Hampshire

'I am a very old woman '*   **12**
Deborah Ann Kilgour
St Patrick's Catholic Junior School
Workington
Cumbria

A Lament for a Dead Baby Bird   **12**
Helena Claire Leeson
Ellington County Junior School
Maidenhead
Berkshire

Area*   **12**
Fiona Katrina Parsons
Lydgate County Primary School
Batley
West Yorkshire

Under the Sea   **13**
Linda Christine Tubb
Queens Road County Primary School
Cheadle Hulme
Greater Manchester

Valkerie   **13**
John Richard Pulford
The Boys' High School
Colchester
Essex

The Mask*   **14**
Caroline Anne Ross
Wessex Gardens Junior School
London NW11

The Tramp*   **14**
Sean Theobold
Shears Green County Primary Junior School
Northfleet
Kent

Nine to twelve years

Internal Journey   **15**
Mark Richard Stevens
Pryford County Junior School
Nr Woking
Surrey

My Entomological Memories 16
Roger John Carruthers
Glebe House School
Hunstanton
Norfolk

Belfast Saturday* 17
Jenni Russell
Eaton (City of Norwich) School
Norwich
Norfolk

Ice 20
Amanda Jane Childs
The High School
Wellington
Telford
Shropshire

Mr Harrieesataremsaa 21
Catherine Lorna Gray
Stranmillis Primary School
Belfast
Northern Ireland

The Stone Ring* 21
Simon Jones
Abingdon School
Oxfordshire

My Gran Sleeping* 22
Jane Elizabeth Bruce
Rothwell County Junior School
Kettering
Northamptonshire

My Girl Friend* 22
Robert Stanley Jarrold
Harrowfield Secondary Modern School
Harold Hill
Romford
Essex

For Sale : a Witches Ashes 23
Sandi Louise Bain
Brighton & Hove High School
Sussex

Trespassing
Amanda Jane McCardie
Dean Close Junior School
Cheltenham
Gloucestershire

25

An Injured Wasp
David John Barrett
Hamstead Primary Schoo
Great Barr
Birmingham

27

Mother*
Simon Prentice Target
Cumnor House School
Danehill
Nr Haywards Heath
Sussex

27

Mouse
Stephanie Anne Wilkes
Ulverston Victoria High School
Ulverston
Cumbria

28

My Hand
Sarah Margaret Tidy
Ashford Grammar School for Girls
Kent

28

Scraping the World Away*
Clive Herbert Webster
St Joseph's R.C. School
London NW10

29

The Cow and Calf
Gillian Mary Lee
The Academy
Ardrossan
Ayrshire
Scotland

30

Argument or Discussion*
Simon Prentice Target
Cumnor House School
Danehill
Nr Haywards Heath
Sussex

31

I Remember* — 32
Brian Robert Mack
The Junior School
St Lawrence College
Ramsgate
Kent

The Desk Safari — 33
Mark Richard Stevens
Pryford County Junior School
Nr Woking
Surrey

The Earth's History* — 34
Murray George Pittock
Abbotswell Primary School
Aberdeen
Scotland

Departed from Love — 39
Jane Cecilia Hamill
St Joseph's Convent
Tamworth
Staffordshire

My Walk Home from School* — 40
Katherine Mary Saunders
Camden School for Girls
London NW5

Birth* — 42
Peter Alan Sirman
The Junior School
St Lawrence College
Ramsgate
Kent

Thirteen to sixteen years

By the Waters of Babylon* — 43
Jes Schooling
Simon Langton Grammar School for Boys
Canterbury
Kent

The New Beginning — 49
Janice Laura Taylor
The Grammar School
Henley-on-Thames
Oxfordshire

Going Home* 53
David Maxwell Young
The Village College
Impington
Cambridge

Not Allowed* 57
Marta Louise Munro
Dundonald Girls' High School
Belfast
Northern Ireland

Dom Cassian* 57
Heather Cresswell
High School for Girls
Gloucester

Bless Me Father 59
Philomena Raftery
Maricourt High School
Maghull
Nr Liverpool

And the Next Morning it was Raining 63
Julie Rachel Dick
Amy Johnson High School
Hull
Humberside

How did I arrive here? 63
Michael George Traynor
St Benedict's School
London W5

Crucifixion* 64
Sally Veronica Partington
Guildford County Technical College
Surrey

The Uncatchable 65
Brian John Warner
The Willian School
Letchworth
Hertfordshire

The Game 67
Maureen Joy Flitton
The Village College
Sawston
Cambridgeshire

Old Age* 69
David Jardine-Smith
King Edward VII School
Sheffield
South Yorkshire

A Prodigy for the Fool* 70
Glyn Rory Williams
Culverhay Comprehensive School
Rush Hill
Bath
Avon

The Pen* 72
Stephen David Hepworth
Cowplain Secondary School
Portsmouth
Hampshire

Nimrod 81
Andrew John Keedwell
Calday Grange County Grammar School
West Kirby
Merseyside

A Miners Wife 87
Roy Mitchell
Lordswood Boys' Grammar Technical School
Birmingham

The Scream* 88
Rosalind Kitchen
Brighton & Hove High School
Sussex

The Inmate 89
Stephen David Leddy
St Mary's College
Great Crosby
Liverpool

Travels in France 92
Imogen Katherine Clout
Sutton High School for Girls
Surrey

The Unicorn and the Television*   92
Kim Taylor
James Allen's Girls' School
London SE22

Spiral of an ill Wind*   93
Milton George Palmer
Kingshurst Comprehensive School
Birmingham

The Game   99
Jonathan George Cox
Bedales School
Petersfield
Hampshire

Boldly I opened the door and went in*   111
Helen Edith Shenton
Alleynes' School
Stone
Staffordshire

I see paper people*   113
Helen Edith Shenton
Alleynes' School
Stone
Staffordshire

Scorpion   114
Pervin Batliwala
Bonner Hill County Sec. School for Girls
Kingston-upon-Thames
Surrey

Awakening*   122
Ann Marie Carlen
Maricourt High School
Maghull
Nr Liverpool

8 years and under

the blue whale

chapter 1

one day there was a blue whale it was the only one in the world men tried to catch it but they got eaten up one day lots of men went out to catch the blue whale they went out but a storm blew up and a man fell overboard and he was drowned and then another man fell in he was drowned too some other people were eaten by sword fish and sharks the next day all the men were sad because their friends were dead the next day they came to the spot where the blue whale was. and suddenly the ship was smashed in to little bits all the men were eaten up but one was not and he swam to an island

chapter 2

when the man got on the island he saw a banana tree and a peach tree and a pear and he found a cave and he lived in it and he found a horse and he stood on the horse to get the fruit one day he found out that his clothes were ragged and he made some other clothes out of leaves and he was very happy with his good clothes they were green he wore his green clothes when he was not working and his old clothes when he was working. he chopped down trees and made a little shelter out side the cave and he made some chairs and after he did that he did not have to do anymore he was so happy that he had a party he had bananas and he made some wine out of grapes by stamping on them and made the wine. the horse had water and some grapes. in the cave he stored all his things in the cave there was treasure but the man did not know

chapter 3

the next day some pirates came they were looking for the treasure the man saw the pirates and he hid in the back of the cave and the pirates did not find the treasure they were sad the man said 'that was close' and then he said 'there must be some treasure here' so he looked for it but he could not find it he was sad too. he had been on the island 2 years he was a bit fed up. the horse gave the man company the man said to him self I do like the island really the next day he found his horse was gone. and he looked for it and some natives had it the man killed the natives. and he got the horse some food and the horse was happy again

chapter 4

that day the pirates came again and they found the man and they tied the man up and they found the treasure too. and they went back on the ship the horse saw this and swam to the boat and jumped on the pirates and knocked them out and then the horse bit the rope and then the man was free and he got the treasure and then he threw the pirates over board and they were drowned and then he swam back to the island and he made a raft and he went down the river suddenly he saw a water fall and his horse pushed a piece of wood in the water and it stopped the raft and the man went a long the piece of wood and he was safe again

chapter 5

that day the horse had a foal and the man made a stable for the horse and the foal and the man lived in the stable with the foal and the horse. the foal soon grew up and then the man had two horses that day the old horse died the man was very sad. he made a big hole and buried the old horse. but he was still a bit happy. the foal made him happy. a storm blew up and the stable fell down and after the storm the man built the stable up again. then the man saw that he had some grains of wheat on him and he planted them and they grew and they grew. and then he got the wheat and put it in the stable and he got the grains and planted the grains again and he did the same thing again

chapter 6

a month later the other horse was hurt and the man made a bandage out of a banana leaf the horse was soon better. the man rode the horse. he liked it when he rode the horse because he could get a round the island faster. he was glad about this he was very glad about it. every day the man went a round the island to get the fruit. one day when the man was chopping a tree down the tree fell on him and the man was nearly squashed but the horse pulled it off and the man said 'thank you'

chapter 7

one day the man saw a ship and it was not a pirate ship and then the man got all his things and got the raft from the water fall and then he said to his horse good bye and then the horse dropt his head and the man walked away sad he got on the raft and went to the ship. and the captain helped the man a board and the man went back to England and he brought back his treasure too and the people on the ship saw the treasure. and when the man was back in England the men and the ship got the treasure but the captain of the ship saw the men and he got a chair and knocked the men out. and then the man said 'thank you' and then he went back to the island because he did not like it in England and he brought some friends with him this time to talk to and they made lots of homes the horse was still there the horse was very hungry but the man saw the horse and he gave it lots of food. the horse was so happy that the man came back that he jumped over the fence and rubd the man's leg with its furry mane and the man patted the horse the horse was so happy that she was crying and the man thought the horse was crying because it was sad and then the man found out that the horse was crying because it was happy and it made him laugh and laugh and the horse did not know why the man was laughing and then the man told the horse and the horse opened its mouth and made a funny nos like this mo me mo me and the man said thats a funny nos and the man laughed again. when the man went out with his friends it remembers the day the man left the island but the horse knows the man will not go away again like he did on the ship

chapter 8

one day the man said to his friends 'I will show you a round the island' his friends said 'yes' so they went and he showed them where the water fall was and then he showed them the sinking sand and then one of his friends fell in the sinking sand and he died and then there was only 2 left and then the man showed the 2 friends the natives home and said they were deserted. and then the man said to his friends are you going to help me bury the natives and they said 'yes' so they did and they buried all the people that died that they can get they buried 20 people and it took them 2 days but they could not get the man in the sinking sand they threw flowers on the sinking sand because they felt that it would make them happy and it did one day they forgot to throw some flowers in the sinking sand and then another man fell in the water fall and he was drowned and then there was only 1 man left. the next day the 2 men were working when the tide was out and they found the pirates bodies and they buried them in their grave yard and now there was 40 people in their grave yard the men's homes were made out of banana leaves by weaving them and then they put another coat of banana leaves and then they pegged it down and it was finished the stable was made out of trees one day John had a birthday John is the one that found the island first. and Jack gave John some bananas and some grapes and they had a little party and they had the bananas and the grapes too

chapter 9

one day the two men were working along and they were working throwing bushes and they saw some thing brown move in the bushes and then they saw it was a brown bear and then they saw lots of them and they ran back to the camp and got their guns and shot all the bears except one and that bear was scratching the horse and then the men shot the bear and it fell down and died and then the man put banana leaves a round the horse. and it was a month before the horse could move. and they buried the bears in the grave yard and the grave yard was nearly full there was only enough room for 4 people to go in there or 4 animals one day the water was all over the island except for the mens homes and the horses stable. when the men got out of their homes they saw all the water they were very surprised and he said 'look' to the other man and the other man said 'yes' that morning the two men went fishing and one of the men fell in the water and he saw that they had caught a dolphin and then the man swam up to the surface and told the other man and they cut the fishing net and they played with the dolphin one day a man said to the other man I am going to tell the dolphin to take us to Africa so the dolphin did and they have lived there ever since then. do you think the dolphin is clever ?

MARTIN ROBERT VANNER 7

Who Is It

Swimming in and out among the branching, many coloured coral were many fish of suprising beuty. Seaweed swayed in the gentle lapping of the waves. On the sand lay beutiful shells that glistened in the tropical sunlight. Suddenly the afternoon stillness was broken by a loud blast on a sea trumpet. A rainbow coloured sea serpent glided in among the shadows. On its back rode a golden haired, green tailed mermaid with an extremely beutiful face. Sper-losh. All the smaller fishes swam away in fright as a shadow fell on the sand of the sea bed. Next moment an arm scooped up the Mermaid Princess and all was still. Then an elderly salmon spoke up. Let us go, he roared, to the palace. Of one order they all swam off to tell King Neptune. Fins thrashed the water and gills bubbled madly. Even the smallest fishes managed 200 miles an hour. Huge whales, sharks and narwhales led the group of angry fish in the right direction. Flying fish skimmed along on the edges of the mass. Soon the magnificent palace came in sight. The salmon who had suggested the swim was sent ahead to ask for an audience of the king. Soon a kingly figure in pink seaweed, coloured pearls and silver appeared. A silvery beard flowed over the jewel studded breast and gave Neptune an aptly kind expression which greatly suited his nature. When he was told of the loss of his daughter he sighed and then blew a small silver trumpet.

Instantly the sea above their heads grew rough. It swept inland for many miles. Presently it brought back the mermaid and her captor. The strange human in his diving suit caused rather a stir among the waiting, wathing group of fish that hovered around Neptune. The Mermaid Princess was glad to see her father but did not know much about the man who had caught her. He himself was no more helpful. From that day onward things went wrong in Merland. The store of silver in the Coral Cave became inaccessible due to a fall of dead seaweed. The coral polyps went on strike. The pearl harvest was not good and the royall sea serpent sprained its tail two days before an important procesion. Everyone was asking the same question. Who is it? Who is doing it? Every one was worried. Eventually the diver was found guilty and warned. He went far away but still the mishaps continued. This was outrages. Every one said so. At last a good shark hid away to wath and saw a strange sight. Dozens of octopuses were walking along the narrow coral ledges. Out came the shark and a moment later they were in handcuffs. Next morning they were found guilty of treason and put to death.

RACHEL HOWE 8

The Adventures of Tiny Tim Mouse

Once there was a mouse called Tiny Tim. One day Tim was asleep when a Fly came up and stole his head but put his eyes back, the Fly took his head away to a witch to make a mask. She was going to use his head as an eye (she had all ready got one eye from another mouse).

Tiny Tim Mouse had woken up by now. He looked at himself in the mirror to see if he'd grown taller in the night but he wasn't as tall. He looked in the mirror and said is that really me but he couldn't hear (he wasn't saying anything).

He walked off to seek his fortune.

He walked straight into the witches cave. The cauldron thought he was a visitor because he looked frightening without a head. He climbed up to get his head but knocked a plate on the witches head. The witch woke up and put him in a cage. She put the key on her bed. But the other mouse without a head came to get his head back.

Then he saw Tim and made a clay Sculpture of him. He put it in the cage with Tim. Then he grabbed the key, locked the door and put the key back.

Then they both ran.

The witch didn't realise that he'd gone at first but she did in the end.

Tim didn't know this district he was lost. He tried one way but it led into some woods. He tried another but it led to a ghost, so he ran.

He ended up back at the witches cave. She locked him up in a cage. He called for help. But the witch stopped him.

Then the witch saw that the sink was dirty so she went shopping for Soapy Soap Suds Super Silver Sink Soap Powder Spells.

Poor Tiny Tim Mouse couldn't call for help because the witch had cast a spell on him. Now what was he going to do, he was guarded by the witches winged monkeys so he couldn't get away. He decided to go to sleep but the witch came back and she decided to turn him into a cat so that he would catch the other mouse. So when he woke up he felt funny, he didn't feel like a mouse.

The witch did the washing up with her new washing powder.

But her winged monkeys were having a feast of bananas and the witch slipped on the skins with the washing powder all over her.

Now everyone knows that soap powder destroys witches so Tim went back home.

It was Tims Birthday he got a hat from his mum and dad and some shrinking and growing powder from his friend mouse.
He made his hat grow with the growing powder then put his presents in and got in himself. He sailed away through the river. But his growing powder fell in the water and a fish gobbled it up.
Because the fish ate the powder his inside grew too big so he burst and his brain flew out so he ate things like necklaces and gold jewellery.
It made him go straight into a Fishermans net.
Meanwhile Tim had reached a restaurant, he made the hat shrink and put it on. Then he realised he'd dropped the growing powder and he couldn't get back. He decided to make the most of it by buying a fish. But he bought the fish with his powder in, so he took the fish and made the hat back into a boat then sailed away.
When he got back to his hole he ate the fish and inside he saw all the money, rings, necklaces, and lots and lots of different kinds of priceless jewels.

PAUL STEPHEN BARNED 8

The Deep Pond

I fell into a deep pond
Down and down I floated
I saw faces on strings
    and skeletons dancing
I was scared
I screamed
But I never heard myself.
I never felt the water
    although it was there.
I landed with a bump
I waited to see what would
        happen.
Then out jumped creatures
    rather like diddy men.
Every thing was alive.

MICHELE HUTCHINSON 8

7

The Skull

It is very old.
It has holes all over it like rats holes.
Its whole head is like a skeleton with horns on it. The cracks in the skull like lightening going all ways. Its horns are like hangle-bares on a bike. I feel sad for that poor animal.

MARTIN MILES BAUL 7

The Serpent

The serpent comes
seven heads
greatly fanged
slithery serpent
seven heads
gard a diamond
glowing bright
seven heads
on seven necks
swaying necks
like branches
in the wind.

SHAUN MATTHEW CHAPLIN 8

My Muddly Bed

'My bed's muddled mum'
'Won't you come up?'
She says she's busy
And dad's having sup

'My bed's muddled mum'
'Won't you come upstairs?'
She says she won't
And Dad hardly cares.

'My bed's muddled Mum'
'Oh won't you hurry?'
Mum says she shan't
And dad's making curry.

8

'My bed's in a muddle mum'
'Oh for goodness sake.'
Mum's in the kitchen
Helping Dad make a cake

'My bed's in a muddle mum'
She hardly hears.
She sits there gazing
As if she hasn't got ears.

'My bed's in a muddle mum'
'Oh, for goodness sake, mum,'
She just sits there
as if she's dumb.
WON'T SOMEBODY MAKE
MY BED!

SALLY LYNN CLARK 8

The Sky at Night

The sky at night
is like a velvet
quilt as black as a rook
and as silent as a fish
and scaterd with golden
sequins and in the middle
somewhere is a silver
rose.

HELEN LOUISE GARRICK 8

I'll Finish It

Although I know my life is wrong.
Although my task is long.
I'll finish it you'll see you will.
I'll finish it and money spill.
I'll finish it and monster kill.
I'll finish it I will you'll see.
I'll finish it and you'll love me.

SAIRA ELIZABETH SHAH 8

The River

The river is dazzling like diamonds,
The water rippling, rippling, by,
The golden lilies all afloat,
Broken adrift by the boat,
Passing through the rustling reeds,
Fishes splashing, ripples in the
    gentle swaying breeze,
The birds chirruping in the trees
Reflections in the dazzling water,
Till it reaches the sea,
Rivers carry nature around
Just waiting there for me,
The whirls of pattern in the light,
Show up bright in the night,
It is getting dark,
Not the time for picnics,
See the sunset fall,
No sound at all.

HAZEL CRANE 7

In the beginning

It was dark
Thick dark
Like soot
Black paper King of dark
Like the dark under your desk
Not a friendly dark
Like in the night
As dark as dirt
As dark as in space
In the beginning
It was just dark
No trees
No water
No people
No food
No bushes
No World
Just dark

ALAN PATERSON DIXON 7

Sounds

In school the squeaking of a chair on
  the floor
Makes me shiver.
Loud noises outside in the playground
Cars in the street and poeple shouting
Workmen yelling clanging banging
Go right through my ears.
Quiet noises like a birds wings in the sky
And there little feet on the ground,
The trees rustle
Little somethings in a hedge
Make me feel nice.
They stay inside my head
And make me think.

JULIE KELFORD 8

The Flood

The crow with his croaky voice,
Said 'oh what a realy deafening noise'.
With the invitations small,
Flew the crow with his cawing call.
'Come get your Invitations here',
Said old Joe crow, to a big black bear.
The Ark is ready HOORAY   HOORAY
It's going to sail away today.
Two by two came animals big,
'Wait for me' said baby pig.
Then the rain came pouring down,
There was no room to move at all.
'Help! the Ark is starting to float',
Bleated a very hungry goat.
Then at the end of the journey long,
There came animals in happy throng.
Noah an altar did build for God,
Out of stick and brick and log.
They all did love him, did they not,
Happy old Noah had saved the lot.

HILARY TERESA SHEPPARD 8

11

'I am a very old woman'

I am a very old woman and I dont get around very much I cant get out of my rocking chair to tell the bread man I want more bread than usual. Today my sister is coming so I am going to finish making my shawl. Tired and weary I pick my knitting basket up. I always use bright colours because I carnt see the pale ones very well. My eyes arent very good now. Then the postman come and knocks at the door. Instead of him leaving the parcel on the step I wave my hand for him to come in. I say to him 'thankyou'. Inside is a letter which says that my sister coudnt come. I got a few little cakes specially and now they'll just go stale. I carnt eat them all. I was looking forward to seeing her I dont see many people nowadays. Now I suppose itl just be another of those dreary old days again. Where did I put that knitting of mine.

DEBORAH ANN KILGOUR 8

A Lament for a Dead Baby Bird

A baby bird is soft and cuddley, but when
it dies it's lumpy and cold.
If you hold it by its leg it droops and hangs
dead as a doormat.
Dead.
Nothing can be done about it
He's dead.
Still as a stone.
Dead.

HELENA CLAIRE LEESON 8

Area

I hate area! I think Mr gatenby hate's teaching it me too. I think he hate's teaching anything except art I love doing art but I suppose we cannot have everything our own way. I work out area by timesing length by width, length is the biggest side and width is the smallest side. I cannot stand the area were you have to take the part away in the middle which mr gatenby calls a garden or a pond. Yesterday mr gatenby said we could not do any christmas things if we did not understand area. Area means an awful lot to me but I just cannot do it.

FIONA KATRINA PARSONS 8

12

Under the Sea

Fish live under the sea
They dart, slide, glide,
Wave, bend, shoot,
Rush, twirl, weave and twist
Whales live under the sea
They thresh majesticly and propel
Water out of their spouts
Crabs live under the sea
They scurry scuttle
Hide under the sand
And move side ways.
Star fish live under the sea
They have little holes under themselves
Their five star fish arms
Cling on to the rocks.

LINDA CHRISTINE TUBB   7

Valkerie

(A poem I wrote after listening to Wagner's *Ride of the Valkerie*)
The soldiers
    wounded
        crying for their mothers
           bloody all over
calling for the Valkerie.
        The Valkerie came soaring through the air.
The wind
    came tormenting on us
        it blew gales, huricanes and storms.
The Valkerie
    came searching for the dead.
        To take them to Valhalla
Here they feasted and boasted of things they had done.

JOHN RICHARD PULFORD   7

The Mask

A Fearsome Mask
Just waiting to be worn
The actor, surprized at such color
and ferociousness
Puts it on quickly
He looks round the room
It looks smaller beacause the eye
holes are tiny
To make the mask more symbolic.
The actor
Rather nervous but used to it
Goes on to the stage
Acts his part as the dragon
With his friend.

CAROLINE ANNE ROSS 8

The Tramp

The tramp
Sits on my
Door step, all alone
An old fine lady
Walks by
And she looks at the old
Tramp.
Then she looks at his clothes
And then she looks
At her clothes
but she walks by.

SEAN THEOBALD 7

Internal Journey

Gazing at the mazed words,
As they slither around the icy page,
Tongue grasping hopelessly at the crazily jumbled syllables.
Slowly the chair judders back on the bony carpet.
With perpetual motion the door swings,
Sweaty hand claws the enamel handle.

Plaster flies as dad's hammer drives home
Gaping a hole in the wall.
Book is placed on a crumpled dust sheet
Amongst the cracked plaster.
Questioning words are blurted at a featureless face
The reply crackles like a bad record.

Head nods; feet turn and diminish.
Door still swinging, chair still swaying,
Clammy hand grasps cool wood.
Tugging madly it bumps defiantly
Terminated abruptly by another saturated limb,
Body swings clumping back into the seat.

Book thumps on the surface,
Eyes return to the now clear words,
Dodging back and forth, scanning the type,
They grind to a halt and zoom in on a word – the focus is lost.
Brow creases into a mountain range
Again the page becomes a dense jungle of words.

MARK RICHARD STEVENS 11

My Entomological Memories

I first became interested in entomology (study of insects) when I was eight. I was introduced to it by a certain Michael Bradshaw. At that time my knowledge of the subject was so little as to be embarassing to mention.

Later Brian Hawkes took me under his wing. He found me firms to help me in the way of equipment and societies to whet my appertite for knowledge of the Animal Kingdom. From him I took my foundations and I owe a lot to him. Now I can look back to the happy days I spent in the forests, marshes, fields, hedgerows, dykes, rivers and seas of Brancaster. His father is rich and owns a lot of Brancaster. Because of this I would always arrive at his house tremendously excited but evilly jealous. He had his marshes, his woods, his farm, his 'laboratory', his mahogany cabinets and his expensive equipment. I had R.A.F. Marham and the little forests and rivers around it. Because of this I had a slightly more difficult and probably better training; training to make the most of what little facilities the surrounding country side had to offer. We had Marham fen, a mixture of rubbish tips and agricultural land with the river Nar in the middle. This was a small heaven in Marham village. By tresspassing several fields one could get here to a wild country full of little unexplored places for one to get lost in. Our walks here were always long as either Tessa, our dog, or I would have disappeared in the tracks of some long gone hare or rabbit. Nothing could hold me in once I aquired the taste for nature. On wet days a certain something would call me to go in search of skulls. A something strange and tempting, something that forced me to leave home and comfort for the blizzards and skulls of the outside world. At times like this I could forget loneliness and cold. Outside lay rewards. At Shouldham Warren for example, I found a bird ring in a sand-martin's nest. This was rewarded by pride. Pride of recognition in the British Trust for Ornithology's files at the British Museum.

When I moved to Thailand my hopes were raised to beyond-belief limits. The giant insects I have seen in these past few years are such that I may never see again. At our yatch club I caught huge beetles and giant moths. I have become a breeder of colossal caterpillars and lovely larvae. The selection of Odonalta (dragonflies) are fantastical. Now I have met a new problem: heat. Wetness and cold cannot stop me but heat can and does. Also I cannot bring myself to catch the lethal hornets that frequent our garden.

And beetles; wow what beetles. Skulls also. I have a snake skull, a turtle skull and a dog skull. I also have two lizard skulls. The snake my father caught in the garden. It was six feet one inch long. The turtle skull my mother found on the beach. The lizards were a gift from our cat. She has killed many of our garden's lizards and has never been very popular for it, on this occaision she was very popular, but only by me.

The dog skull is a story or at least it makes a story. The skull I found on the beach, nothing strange about that but this is a good example of Thailand's foul dog problem. Thailand is overun with diseased, starving or half-dead mongrels. It is a living pet shop but one that is better not seen. I am a keen conservationist and I am very worried about the way that nobody does anything about it.

Yet when I am older I am sure I will still look back at these nostalgic scenes and say 'my knowledge of the subject was so little as to be embarassing to mention.'

ROGER JOHN CARRUTHERS 12

Belfast Saturday

Seven o'clock.

Grey-haired Mrs Collins turned over in her bed, a huge mountain of flesh. The room was stuffy, but she could not open the window because the lock was broken, and there was no-one to mend it since 'He' had died six years ago.

Her alarm-clock went off promptly at seven-five, and she slowly heaved her massive bulk out from underneath the bed-clothes. She dressed herself slowly, shivering in the cold of the unheated room.

.   .   .   .   .

Miss Jeanie O'Flaherty had been up for an hour already. To-night her boyfriend was taking her out, and she had been up early, pressing and ironing her best clothes.

Jeanie looked appraisingly at her reflection in the full-length mirror. She smiled suddenly at herself, then stood stock-still, listening, as she heard the faint rattle of gunfire.

'How far away?' she breathed to herself, hoping desperately, 'not here, Lord, not here, not again.' Last week she had seen a car pass and had watched, helpless, as two young teenage boys were mowed down with bullets. She was shaking now, re-living the terror of that moment, hearing the one boy's scream of agony, watching the other drop to the ground without uttering a sound.

. . . . .

Mrs Collins munched her cornflakes while she listened dispassionately to the news.

'and these murders bring Ulster's civilian death toll to 637, since 1969. Now for the weather.'

She switched the radio off, and continued to eat. Mrs Collins had never been actively involved in the violence, and after the first shocks, when deaths were announced daily, she accepted everything with stoicism.

Fifteen minutes later, she was down on her knees, scrubbing the kitchen floor. Sean Collins had always liked a clean house. His photograph stood on top of the green wooden table in the corner of the room. She was glad that he had not lived to see 'these awful goings-on' as she termed it in her mind.

Breathing heavily, she pulled herself to her feet, took a duster, and polished, gently, the silver photograph frame. Sean Collins' face smiled up at her as she worked.

Carefully she replaced the photograph, and moved on to tidy her minute front-room.

There was nothing to tidy. She ran her duster quickly over the furniture, and sat down to rest in one of the uncomfortable armchairs. The last time any visitor had been in here, she recalled, was when the vicar came to tell her that Sean was dead.

. . . . .

Jeanie was washing up. Her next-door neighbour, Brigit Maloney, Jeanie's own age, was talking eagerly about make-up and dresses. Jeanie placed the last plate in the rack.

'Come upstairs, Brigit, I've laid out my clothes for this afternoon. Andrew's taking me out, you know.'

Brigit admired Jeanie's new dress, which was white-bordered with blue stripes. Jeanie was wearing it now, turning round and round slowly.

'Oh, won't you look lovely tonight!' Brigit breathed. 'Have you any blue eye-shadow? It would go with that ever so well!'

Jeanie shook her head. 'I couldn't afford it before, but I've been saving for three weeks, and I'm going to buy it this afternoon.'

. . . . .

Ten minutes to two.

Mrs Collins, retired charwoman, grey-haired and humble, was out shopping at the nearby supermarket. She peered anxiously at Campbells Soups, threepence off recommended price, or should she buy a packet soup, penny cheaper? She was pondering on the question, when she heard a shrill voice exclaiming:

'Look, Mum, that lady's dress is darned!'

Mrs Collins wished she could disappear. Pretending to be oblivious of the many faces turned in her direction, she continued staring at the soups, but she had never felt so flustered inside since, as a child, she had been made to stand on a stool in front of the school in disgrace.

Miss Jeanie O'Flaherty, shop assistant, off-duty, black-haired and strongly Catholic, looked sympathetically at the old woman, smoothing down her own blue dress while she did so. At three o'clock her boyfriend was coming to take her out, and Jeanie had bought a new dress for the occasion. Now she was running over the merits of different types of make-up in her mind. Only ten shillings to spend, and so many different kinds of lipstick, eyeshadow, cheek-shiner and nail-varnish! Perhaps after all she had better buy that 'Glamor Girl' make-up box. It was *so* hard to decide – Jeanie glanced at the time. Five minutes to two.

Mrs Collins had decided on Campbells Soups. After all, Sean had always preferred tinned soup when they could afford it, and besides, her grandchildren were coming to tea, little Mark, Barbara and Johnny. She thought affectionately of Barbara, nice little girl she was, well-mannered and always polite – one the reasons for visiting the supermarket was to buy a present for Barbara, whose birthday was in two days time. Mrs Collins had saved for a month to be able to afford buying her granddaughter the eleven-shilling doll she wanted.

The old lady glanced down at her unpolished shoes, and wondered if she could afford just a tiny tin of shoe-polish. Mrs Collins found life hard these days, living on a minute pension while prices of goods grew higher and higher.

Jeanie stopped in front of a mirror and patted her hair into place. She looked unseeingly at the mirror, as her boyfriend told her that she was the most beautiful girl in the world. Then she

was literally brought down to earth, as Mrs Collins walked into her. 'Sorry,' Mrs Collins said, and Jeanie was just scrambling to her feet, when –
Two o'clock

The rescue workers dug for three hours before uncovering the bodies. Enough was left of Mrs Collins to be identified, but all that remained of Jeanie was a pile of ashes and a scrap of blue material fluttering forlornly in the wind –

JENNI RUSSELL 12

Ice

The wind had chaperoned the ice and frost
It splintered like confetti over the marsh
The reeds stood stiffly to attention, clothed in white.
The tussocks of grass were strung with filigree bunting
As though for a carnival.
Stunted bushes became graceful brides
Soon it was dawn and the ice took a rosy hue
Like a freezing chameleon.
The pearly sky was fingered by orange talons of light.
The dawn reached a crescendo of light
And fell to a leaden sky
That was as smooth and anonymous as a blank canvas.
Later the snow fell, a million snow-birds
Performing intricate dances as they fell to the earth.
The snow was as crisp as Autumn leaves
It feathered the pine trees on the slopes
Down in the marsh the tiny water-ways froze
Covered in snow, like a sleeping child
                under an eider-down.
The hungry birds nagged at the stony ground
The frogs lay cocooned in mud at the bottom of the marsh.
The moles built commuter ways in the crust of snow
A fox trod delicately among the snow-drifts.
With a gentle sigh, a pine tree shed its load
And straightened up, like an old man.
The day drifted on, sluggish, till night fell –
And declared its curfew. . . .

AMANDA JANE CHILDS 12

Mr Harrieesataremsaa

He walks harry,
He talks tarry,
And sings laralery,
But my girl,
You can't –
You can't scrap him up
Not that Harrieesataremsaa
He got a hobalaloo temper
And a mouth of fire
You can't catch him
Where does he libely
That you make asky
In the woody of Stacarasby
He sit there,
Eating little girlies in the barbateryatsarema rain.
Drat it,
Let me describe him
Xy Osy all upon him
A squibblyribbly heart
So he says,
Drat him Harrieesataremsaa

CATHERINE LORNA GRAY 11

The Stone Ring

As I stare up the hill I see,
The bare stones outlined against the sky.
Like aged sentries waiting to
witness the end of time.
As I trudge up the hill they
appear to turn wizened angry faces towards
me, the disturber of their peace.
Now as I stand in the middle and
gaze around, the forbidding
stones seem to draw around, closing
in with a menacing stare.
Power seems to throb from each stone.
Then I shake my head and
concentrate, and the stones seem to retreat
and back down.

SIMON JONES 12

My Gran Sleeping

In a russet chair with wrinkly patterns,
Lies my Gran,
Her veins plainly visible like seams of Blue John
Piles of soft, plump cushions,
Check, vivid crimson and dull red,
Heaped like a tangled rainbow.

The ancient stool on which her worn,
Tired and weary feet are propped,
Is adjusted to its lowest height.

Her sleep is deep and uninterrupted
Gentle snores issue from her,
Like brief summer thunder.
She has a haggard
Blotchy, loving face.
Paper-thin eyelids
Cover violet, bloodshot eyes.
A clear dusky red mouth
Forms the main feature of her face.
Mellow brown hair frames it.
She has a hooked nose,
Like an eagle's beak.
All in all though she is really quite pretty.

JANE ELIZABETH BRUCE 10

My Girl Friend

I had a girl friend
She was very sweet
In the lower school I sat beside her

My teacher told me off
We were speaking you see
We had to separate
I was very sad

I still saw her though
Arfter school you know
I went round her house once
I was very scared

22

Her Mother oponed the door
She didn't like me
I could tell by her face
She asked me to come in

In side she sat on a chair
And said she is doing her hair
I waited for a little while
And then she came down
I asked her weather she would like to come out
For I had saved some money

I took her to the pictures
We laughed at Donnald Duck
And held in susspence by Aggifa Cristy
Arfter the film we wated till last
For we didn't want to be crushed

I bort her a beef burger
Just to impress
It was very dear
But I thought nothink of it

ROBERT STANLEY JARROLD 11

For Sale: a Witches Ashes

'No, I am *not* a witch, no.' I heard myself say, *why* didn't they understand? All I had done was play with a small doll and talk to my cat.

'You are a witch, aren't you,' exclaimed a cool, calm, plummy voice.

'For *God's* sake . . . *no!*' I am frantic!

'Anna, listen, we know you are a witch, but if you tell us you are a witch, we might not burn you . . . only hang you,' whispered that silky, sickly voice. I screamed!

'No, no, no, leave me be, I am not a witch.' My throat is sore with shouting, tears were burning my cheeks. Frustration was killing me!

'You are a liar.' He was jeering at me! Oh, why did he not get angry, *anything* but this monotonous, velvet voice.

I am too tired to think anymore, my mind will not work.

'I am not a witch, *please* believe me.'

23

Were these really my words, or somebody elses?

I suppose they must be mine.

'Right, you will be burnt tomorrow at . . .'

At this he started flicking through the pages of a book to see (no doubt) when it was possible to have me burnt.

'Well, we could fit you in between Nancy Miller and Selina Cobbler, if that is alright with you?'

Oh, the snake. How I hate. I have never hated so much before. My teeth grind together and my fists were clenched so tightly behind my back that my palms were sweating. 'You murderer, stealer of life, son of death. Why?' My head was raging like a blacksmith's furnace, my throat was rasped and torn with screaming. I could have killed him, only I was tied down. . . . They lead me from the questioning room. Two dim figures, the last people I was ever likely to see again. Two blurred shadows in a short blurred life. *They* sling me into a cell . . . but I feel no pain. I am so numb. Ready for tomorrow, I suppose.

.   .   .   .   .

'Get up witch, stir a foot.'

'Why, is it time for . . .' I awoke and my words were still really part of my sleep.

'Don't be stupid half-wit, it's only morning.'

'Are you sure that is all?'

'No, we want you to identify your cat and your doll.'

'Oh goodness, where are they, please tell me where they are.' Suddenly I was wide awake. These were my dearest treasures! They must not hurt them. They wouldn't dare. What is 'they'? I keep referring to *somebody* as 'they' but I know not, who! Still, that is of no importance, just a silly thought.

'*Here* they are slut.'

'Yes, that's them, let me have them.'

'No, not until you admit you are a witch.'

'But I have told you . . .'

I realised that if I said I wasn't a witch then the things which are dearest to my heart would be hurt!

'Hurry, we have not got all day, you know.'

'Yes, they are mine, and I *am* a witch!'

But I am not a witch! Never mind, my brain is in two parts, thinking and saying, and at the moment the saying part is less confused and has got more common sense. So I will let it lead me.

'Ha, ha, ha, that fooled you, witch.'

24

'What do you mean? I have confessed, so I will only be hanged and you can not hurt Rosie and Midnight now, can you?'

But it was too late, already Rosie my wooden idol was being torn apart, and . . . I puked over the floor, then crouched into a corner and sobbed and sobbed. . . . Numbness . . . Midnight is dead, Rosie has been torn apart. I am being lead to the fire and Nancy Miller's shrieks are still flavouring the air. I walk up the pile of dying embers, slipping now and again on a rolling branch, till I reach the pole in the centre of the pile.

Only a fraction of my mind is still in working order, the rest is already dead.

A few minutes prayer. But I do not pray. I scorn that word. *They* have made me believe I actually *am* a witch, so I have no hope of heaven. The branches are lighted. A warm glow is in my heart, and my feet are on fire! What a strange feeling to look down and see your knees on fire. Burning brightly then giving way as the flames eat through the bone. A smile appears on my face and my belly heaves with inward laughter. Or is it crying I know not. . . .

Blackness . . . Deadness . . . I am no more. I have no soul, mind or heart. Just ashes mingling with the ashes of wood and Nancy Miller.

SANDI LOUISE BAIN 12

Trespassing

It was a cold, slippery blue winter evening. I was walking home from a friend when it suddenly grew dusky, and just a bit frightening. The grass was frosted hard. My breath hurt my throat. Little dead birds for whom the Winter had proved too much lay frosted to the road, dead in the worst possible way, they were frigid like little rocks lying forlorn and forgotten on the road.

My whole face stung with cold and my head ached.

I stumbled on a brick-like ridge of ice. Then I decided to just cut across a private field and not go home the long way.

I looked round to see if anyone was watching me.

I swung a leg over the hedge separating the field from the road.

I could hear my heart beating loudly.

That field was covered in snow. It dazzled my eyes. I couldn't decide whether it was beautiful or not.

It was intoxicating. I could feel myself being drawn to it.

But part of me shrank back.

I ignored it.

I began to feel big and brave. I half laughed. It was fun. I was trespassing. At least, it was fun at first.

But half way through I was frightened. It was beginning to get very dark. Also, what would happen if I was being watched? What if someone found me trespassing. My footprints. What if somebody saw those? I wanted perhaps my father to come and find me. To come and hold my hand. Just to feel warmth after all that coldness. I was beginning to panic.

I was still laughing. It wasn't a very nice laugh. It wasn't a laugh that I had ever laughed before. It was a forced laugh. It was choking, frightened. I was pretending I wasn't frightened. I was bold, I was brave. I didn't care.

The cold laughed back at me. I wished that I had gone home the long way. 'You're not frightened,' laughed the coldness. 'You're enjoying it.' I almost shouted.

I wasn't crying. It was worse than crying. It was as if all the tears were frozen hard inside me.

I couldn't forget that I was trespassing. The air was thick with coldness and that coldness whispered.

'Someone is watching. Someone has seen. Someone knows you're trespassing.'

And the cold laughed again. So high that it hurt my ears to hear it. The cold had surrounded me. It clawed at me. It grasped me.

I heard a sound behind me. Someone was behind me. Someone must have caught me trespassing. For a second I couldn't move.

And then I ran. I ran and ran until I had to push the air inside to breathe. I fought the cold. I felt sick with cold and running. And unknown footsteps pounded behind me.

And suddenly I felt the worn gate at the end of the field. I climbed over.

I stood for a minute over the gate to hear the footsteps. I heard none. Puzzled I looked back. There were no footsteps besides my own.

I laughed. It was an easy laugh. My home was right next door. The tears melted and streamed down my face in happy relief. I had been chased – yes. By my own conscience.

AMANDA JANE McCARDIE 11

26

An Injured Wasp

He can not fly,
   but his wings are reaching for the sky and trying to pull his
too-heavy body up into the blue world above.
   His shivering wings make a sound like my dads shaver.
I wonder where he comes from, and how did he hurt his wing?
I let him crawl on my finger, and hope he will not sting me.
All six legs chase after one another.
The tips of his legs feel gentle and itchy as he struggles across
my hand. I have to scratch my palm.
His lovely body is sunflower-striped, and his head is streamlined,
with big staring eyes that don't move.
   In my hand he seems quite content, not struggling, so I feel
his head delicately with the tip of my first finger.
   The tiny hairs feel like soft cotton, and the wings are like cracked
glass. If I place him carefully on a yellow flower his hurt wing
might heal.

DAVID JOHN BARRETT 10

Mother

A lovable creature.
Sympathetic in her own cosy way.
Aware of the world
With its shadows of blood.
A strong personality.
A clear, loud, voice.
But sometimes so quiet
So tender
So gentle,
Yet not weak.
Understands without note,
Without quiver.
A telephone directory for a brain:
Numbers, columns, birthdays,
Registration numbers,
Just facts.
Non fuss.
Dustproof, noise proof, dirt proof
But not playing-the-piano-with-
unwashed-hands-proof.
NO!

SIMON PRENTICE TARGET 10

27

Mouse

It's had the run of this house, for three long days,
The cleaner handed in her notice yesterday.
'But it's only a baby,' I protested
When we found her, in fits of hysteria on the landing.
It was really quite funny the way it scuttled
Into the back of the dog,
Who sniffed and licked, and walked away.
'That dog is going!' warned my father, as it
Sat and watched the cheeky little trespasser
Play 'ring-a-roses' round the chair legs.

But this morning I found it, spattered with drops
Of dull-red blood.
Two small beady eyes, bulging, they stare at me.
Surprised? Astonished? But not afraid.
The cruel wire springs shut with a
Crunch of small bones, there is no time for
Fear.
Or is there?
Perhaps he was caught round his silky-soft stomach
And stayed there, in pain, and agony,
Only to be found in the morning and burned
With the rubbish.
                    What did he do?

                                        STEPHANIE ANNE WILKES 12

My Hand

With my flesh hand,
I gather up the brush,
Guiding the brush into paint.
My hand steers swiftly that way
With a forte stroke;
A sudden change takes place.
I can make patterns,
Beautiful in their private lines.
My hand the navigator.

                                        SARAH MARGARET TIDY 12

Scraping the World Away

Every day
I feel like getting on my knees
And scraping the world away.
But what would the people think
If they saw the world disappearing
Into my finger nails?
What is under it all?
A ball of fire?
I think it's the same with people
If you scrape away the bones,
Hatred and blood.
What's left?
Only the kindness of a flower.
But what will happen to the people?
They will get scraped away
Just like the dirt.
But the sky,
How will I scrape that away?
I'll climb a ladder to the top
And pull it all down
But when I've scraped it
Where will I put it all?
Where will I put myself?
I'll lock myself in a cage
And drift away
Or might throw it all in the
BURNING FIRE
and nothing will be left
And I'll start again on another planet.

CLIVE HERBERT WEBSTER 10

The Cow and Calf

While looking through a magazine
I saw a picture
A picture of a cow and calf
They looked so peaceful and gentle
Yet, when I looked at the article
And read a little
I found that the story wasn't so peaceful
It was a true story about a town
A little town
As small as the calf
Which is surrounded by war
The war in Vietnam
Yet the people have to go on living
Living with the war
The war, so near that bombs can be heard falling
Bringing injury, destruction and death
While men in far off countries
Safe, in their ten roomed houses
With colour televisions
Decide their fate.
The cow and calf
Gently licking each other
Are the sign of a party
A party in the local election
They were holding an election
While people were dying close by
Dying horribly
I carry on reading
Somewhere in war-torn countries
Babies are going hungry
Dying of malnutrition
While I am reading
Of a local election.

GILLIAN MARY LEE   12

Argument or Discussion?

'Ah-ha I see the figures of Hell have risen,' said Lucifer pointing to a small register. 'I claim to have more people sent here from the 99 fork than you have sent to your place.' Lucifer laughed. '$369\frac{1}{2}$ people killed this year and only $2\frac{1}{2}$ people have gone up to your place.' The Lord grunted. 'That means,' he continued. He paused momentarily to do some quick calculations, 'er . . . um,' he uttered. Then, 'Ah yes, that means ha! ha! that old Beelzebub up at the 99 fork will have been pretty busy this year. He will have been able to point here in Hell when judgement comes 367 times, and only be disgusted and point up to heaven $2\frac{1}{2}$ times. You see, nowadays everyone does wrong, nothing is right, all wrong, even these figures in this register are wrong, cheated by me, I mean, oh dear, I got slightly carried away, dear me!'

The Lord rose from the table he was sitting at with Lucifer and leaned over the edge of the cloud to view his world.

'The contrast between good and evil is great, for the evil is intensely inferior to Good. If it wasn't for that 4th line in that recipe that I found called World there would be no evil, bad, sins and other such things. No Lucifer for that matter either. 'I still have some,' said the Lord applying a little self control. 'I still have the man who lives at No. 6, Portsmouth Avenue.' He paused, then filled with rage swung round and hit the table sharply with his fist. 'Beelzebub gives biased judgements anyway. If I'd won the toss I'd have my biased representative at the 99 fork, you'd be surprised what Gabriel can do,' said the Lord.

'Ha! Ha!' cackled the devil. 'I have everything in the world, even proverbs. Have you heard my latest? . . . Revenge is sweet. And I didn't make that up. Man did, your man,' said the devil mimicking the Lord's voice. 'Man is right for once, man makes good decisions and writes bad proverbs.'

'Revenge is positively sour,' whispered the Lord. 'You contradict yourself, devil,' said the Lord calmly. 'You say man is right and makes good decisions, yet how come you state man is absolutely wrong. Define your terms, devil.'

'Er, well I suppose so. Oh well, er, um, yes . . . well, you see?'

'Distinctly not!' replied the Lord without even raising his voice.

The devil rose to a huge temper, the blood broiled beneath his skin. He put his hand to his knife and carressed its blade. God's back was to him. It would be so easy to eliminate, – God. Just one gentle stab, it wouldn't take long and would be a quick way to die. Lucifer crept up behind him. 'Yes,' he said, his knife glinting in the sun. He leapt onto the Lord and struggled violently. The Lord swung round, snatched his knife and tipped him over the cloud. He hung from the cloud by his left hand. The Lord put his foot gently on Lucifer's hand. Lucifer looked to his death far below. The Lord helped him up. 'I can't believe it,' stuttered the devil. 'You helped me up. I attempted to kill you!' Astonished the devil looked the Lord in the face. 'You're too good, I – I can't b-bear it.' The devil went mad and fell off the cloud. 'Love thy neighbour,' uttered the Lord. Promptly there was a thunderstorm.

SIMON PRENTICE TARGET 10

I Remember

I remember the day when my mother was out, I stood on a chair next to the bath with only one needle underneath the taps, and taking the top off the bottle of 'Baby Disprin', I thought, 'If I eat that one she'll notice, and if I eat that one she'll notice too.' So after much thought I ate all of them, 33, counted out by our doctor with red hair up his nose, forcing a rubber tube down my throat as I wriggled, spewing up baked beans, Disprin and spaghetti all over the nurses with up side down watches.

I remember coming home from school at four o'clock after an unsuccessful day of trying to pull little girls' knickers down and seeing who could piss highest up the wall and getting clipped round the lug hole so hard that I cried all the 49 bus journey home for pinching a stick of Bubble gum from the shop at the corner that sold sherbet instead of lemonade powder.

I remember playing football with the big boys on the beach and getting the football kicked in my face and everyone was sorry and kind. I sulked and dug my hands into the sand and pulled out a watch with 21 jewels and the date and everyone was jealous and nasty.

I remember the taste of soap used to wash my mouth out for swearing at the babysitter who took me to Dreamland where I won a man on a parachute by turning the ducks over and seeing which one had the highest number stamped on its runt.

I remember a girl with black hair who I liked who went to the dentist to have a filling but he made a hole through her tongue with the drill I hate because it screams almost as loudly as I do when I visit the place I mustn't mention because it makes my sister cry.

I remember going to a beautiful cathedral but I can't remember where and I can't remember what it looked like, there was a very interesting exhibition, I don't know, what it was about but there was a picture, a man pulling a jagged knife through a brown cow's throat and he smiled, he glared at the bleeding corpse like a mad man. I'll always remember that glare, it made me feel greasy and guilty and angry.

I imagine my mind as the rings of a tree stump. The core of my mind is a searchlight. I search all round my mind for memories but they sometimes hide. All the memories that once hid but now I have found, I guard and prize as my greatest treasures. But things that happen lately are shy and hide beyond the distance of the searchlight where they die and rot never to be remembered again.

BRIAN ROBERT MACK 12

The Desk Safari

A stampeding rush, bustling, pushing, shoving
You must find a decent desk.
The hunt begins.
No not there, that's next to Bill,
Over there, Oh beaten to it,
Ah a vacant double
Quick Phil over here hurry.
Heck! that's all you need Davids got the place next to you,
Well you'll have to put up with him:
Now examine the desk.

A name, Paul Rivers, imprisoned for eternity in the varnish.
A horizontal motorway runs undeviatingly across the desk.
A yacht sails doggedly on, racing a tortoise.
A devilish pupil has hollowed out a gallows.
Deeply chisled MAN,
Another hand has scratched Women in bored retaliation.
A test cheater scrawled February.
An equilateral triangle floats idly in space.
On the underside two flags flutter jubilantly.
On the painted hinge a map of Africa drawn by a future explorer.

MARK RICHARD STEVENS 11

The Earth's History

I

A whirling cloud of whitish-greenish gas,
      Pulsing, throbbing,
Whirling faster and faster,
      Inwards, Outwards
Pulse, Heave,
      Round and round,
Faster and faster.
      Tails of gas,
Shooting off into space.
      Faster yet,
And rings appear,
      Faster,
Let us look closer
      In one of these rings,
The third one out
      A red-hot gas-ball is spinning and slowing.
Oceans and continents,
      Appear on its surface
Heaving and changing.

2

Six hundred million years ago,
      A cold wind blowing over hard rocks,
And a warm sea sheltering amoeba,
      The start of life.
Five – Twenty million years ago
      A Cambrian sea lapped over,
The Trilobites,
      The thick civilisation of small creatures,
        Below the sea.
Four – Sixty Five ago,
      Beneath the Ordovician Sea,
Huge Nautilids,
      With long cone shells,
Ate the scampering Trilobites as they ran,
      And life under water grew greater and greater in extent.

Three – Fifty Million years ago,
    In the Silurian Time,
Plants, tiny organisms, were thrown up on the land,
    And survived,
And beneath the sea fish began.
    None more than fifteen centimetres long.
Three – Twenty Million years ago,
    In the Devonian Time
Ponds dried and fish crawled through the mud over land,
    To the next pond,
And so ever so slowly developed legs.
    And amphibians appeared,
Back in the depths of sea,
    Dinicthys reigned king,
And was the terror of every living thing.

Two – Sixty-Five Million years ago,
In Carboniferous Time,
    Smelly swamps covered the land
And trees fell in and made the coal,
    Amphibians thrived,
And Eryops lived and died.
    Huge dragonflies buzzed through the slime,
And amphibian spawn floated on it at the same time.
    Two – Fifteen millions ago,
A Permian Sun beamed down,
    On a Dimetrodon sunning in the sand,
A squeal, a shuffle,
    A squeak, a roar,
And poor old Eryops is no more.
    One Ninety-Five ago,
Amid Triassic's luscious plants,
    Dinosaurs begin to show,
Plateosaurus, his head wagging 6 metres off the ground,
    Munches through the luscious plants
While the defeated Phytosaur raves and rants.

One – Seventy million years ago,
        Amid Jurassic's jungled plants,
As Brontosauri munch and crunch
        And Allosaurus eats his lunch.
In a Jurassic swamp,
        A Brontosaur eats near a bank,
Too near,
        For look!
An Allosaur is creeping,
        Crouching,
Springs!
        Tearing at flanks,
Slashing at windpipe,
        Lashing of tail,
The crunching of the head, and,
        Brontosaurus lies dead on the sand.

6

One – Forty millions ago,
        A Gorgosaur warily circles Monoclonius,
In a Cretaceous clearing,
        A lunge, a growl, a snap,
Another lunge, too close,
        A yap.
Although in pain,
        The carnivore circles again,
He tears the backbone out,
        And rips out the windpipe,
Eats the dying animal
        By night,
All that is left of the bloody scene,
        Is a skeleton and some dried blood.

7

Eighty million years ago,
        A Triceratops eating by a muddy-bank
Suddenly a crash rings through the trees,
        A Tyrannosaurus lunges towards the herbivore,
The ground shaker,
        Another lunge,

The wound is deep,
　　　　No-one will disturb Tyrannosaurus as he eats.
An Anklyosaur munches through the grass.
　　　　Two days later,
Another tremendous crashing,
Tyrannosaurus has come for another meal.
　　　　On the outside the Anklyosaur looks well protected,
But all Tyrannosaurus needs to do is to get a foot under him,
　　　　To turn him over,
This Tyrannosaurus cannot do,
　　　　Because of limited intelligence.
So he only gets a nasty knock on the head,
　　　　Instead.

8

Sixty million years ago,
　　　　A groaning Tyrannosaurus,
Rolls over and over,
　　　　Dying slowly,
Already skeletons of other beasts lie strewn upon the ground,
　　　　Nothing to eat,
Starving to death,
　　　　A cheekly furry animal scuttles by.
Tyrannosaurus dies.
　　　　This is the End of Dinosaurs.
And now mammals will take over the earth.

9

The Eocene Dawns
　　　　Sixty million years ago,
Tiny Eohippus, dawn horse,
　　　　Runs about on his four toes,
He is scarcely bigger than a terrier,
　　　　Compare him to the Dinosaurs!
Most of the Dinosaurs are gone,
　　　　But other reptiles still live on.
Crocodile, turtle, snake, lizard,
　　　　But these are outclassed in the Eocene world,
A hoot through the trees,
　　　　An ape,
The shape of things to come.

10

Oligocene, Miocene, Pliocene, Pleistocene.
  Twenty-Six – 500,000 years ago,
The greatest animal of the Oligocene,
  Was the Brontotherium,
Roamer of the North-American Plains,
  Whom the Indians called Thunder-Horse,
Five metres long and three metres high,
  In the Pliocene the biggest mammal lived,
The Balucatherium plodded the Earth,
  7·5 metres tall,
Weighing 11 tons.
  In the Pleistocene dwelt the huge mammoth
With tusks of a six metre span,
  But since then all have been pushed out,
By the new creature, man.

11

Man began, Proper man,
  With Australepithecus.
Two millions ago,
  And since then they have grown.
Copper Age, Bronze Age, Iron Age,
  Have passed between then and now.
Remember,
  When you meet a business man in the street,
His ancestors:

> CRO-MAGNON
> SWANSCOMBE
> Neanderthal
> Australepithecus
> Ape
> Dinosaur
> Reptile
> amphibian
> fish
> trilobite
> amoeba
> cell

MURRAY GEORGE PITTOCK 11

Departed from Love

I learnt in the dust what life was about, pondering with my thoughts.

It seemed to me I was disguising myself in a multitude of innocence. But really in my labyrinthine mind I was a human with natural instincts that were never unveiled. My friends and the people that surrounded me crowned my head with considerate thoughts. But I never really found myself. Why is life full of surprises? Why can I not discover the secrets of love? Fate is pushed in an unkind way, the corners of life are unexpected. I did not know what life was like without love and understanding. I recalled that it was high, long, and never meeting an end.

Height and length mattered not in these circumstances nature and fate helped. Stealthy, slaving and encrouched did our love end.

Under the beeches with naked white limbs, and the bird flying south did I realise I was flying in a trance away from my dreams. The grass choked with stones and the trees' roots stretched across the surface. The wall of our love was masked with ugly shrubs that could not be burned without complete renewal. Our ivy love was sprawled everywhere, he was like a jewel in my hand and I in his, until we parted for ever. Standing beneath the naked copper beech he uttered his last kiss. Upon a fine Autumn day with the birds at rest, we departed, I was now a dead nettle in his heart, with no meaning.

She threw her enchantment upon him, he was like a vessel waiting to be filled. He and I had our moments, but she would descend upon him like a hawk that never failed to catch its prey. She was glad I was now got rid of, I was an obstacle standing in the way.

My heart pounds with hatred, anger and jealousy when I see them. It is just an ordinary lover's emotion that will never fail. My life is empty now, each day I walk in the wilderness among nature for remembrance but nought comes to me as I am now departed from love, the plants are renewing but I cannot renew myself.

JANE CECILIA HAMILL 12

39

My Walk Home from School

Walking home from school
Is when I feel happiest.
I never remember the days when the rain pours down,
but only the days when the back view gently melts away
into the distance surrounded by sunshine.
It doesn't care about me going,
for the next morning
the unfortunate pupil,
who walks silently up the road,
will again be greeted by this grim fortress of learning,
where pens squeak,
ink is spilt,
and mathematics are enforced
from nine till four.
But I like walking home.
I walk with my friends down Patshull road,
or down the road whose name I do not know,
where the pavement is always being repaired,
and there is nothing to walk on but sand and puddles.
I walk past a building
where a solitary workman
sings snatches from Carmen.
He shouts 'Hello darlin'!'
As I walk past, not caring that my nose is in the air.
My clogs echo on the blissful street.
I can feel my homework in my bag.
On the corner they are building
yet another monstrosity,
another building to offend the graceful streets of London.
Sometimes a sly wind
comes racing round the corner,
and lifts my hair around my collar.
I turn to Kentish Town Road,
which is a turmoil of traffic,
and I meet streams of schoolgirls,
running for buses.
They wear clogs like me,
you can hear them clatter down the road.
'Can't stop now, I've got to go. That's my bus, there,
the 134.'

The bus is like a dinosaur
that swallows up hurrying people,
and spits out tickets.
My bus rears in the crawling traffic
like an impatient stallion.
It comes to a grinding halt.
I step on,
and end my conversation
with the girl who takes a different bus.
I often like to go upstairs,
to see if I can grab that corner seat.
An old woman is sitting there.
Shall I sit next to her?
No.
I prefer to sit alone.
The Irish bus conductress comes upstairs.
I dislike this woman who asks me if I'm under Fourteen.
I see her so often,
surely she must know by now.
It is my joy to ring the bell,
and feel the joy of making the bus stop.
Crossing Dartmouth Park Hill,
with its heavy traffic.
Past the Church.
I'm home.
I knock on the door
'Oh it's Kate!' I hear my mother shout
'Get off your backsides, you lot, let her in!'
A sigh of 'Oh no!'
shuffling of feet.
Could any homecoming be so sweet?

KATHERINE SAUNDERS 12

Birth

It lay there
A small brown oval.
It heaved out and
Bulged. A little hole
Appeared.
The shell around
Began to push back
Like minute tidal waves.
Cracks reached out like
Tentacles across the
Fragile surface.
They slowly widened
Like an earth splitting up.
More tidal waves
Swirl across the surface.
Pieces of shell fly out in
All directions as the hole
Widens.
The interior hurls
Itself at the air.

Rolled up in a
Bundle among
The wreckage of the
Shell lay a little heap of
Yellow.

PETER ALAN SIRMAN 12

13-16 years

By the Waters of Babylon . . .

The bell for the end of the school day rang. Mrs Richards, the English teacher, cut off in mid-sentence, sat down resignedly; she wasn't even going to try to stop the surge as the members of her form rushed to get out of the class, out of the school and on to the streets where they were in their element. She looked at the most troublesome pupil, a tall coloured boy, pushing everyone out of his way as he made for the door. One of his friends called out to him:

'Hey, Leroy!'

'What you want, man?' the boy said in a surprisingly thick West Indian accent – surprising because he had lived in Britain all his life.

'You going out tonight?' asked his friend.

'Where to, man?'

'Sundown. Duke Reid, he on tonight.'

'Where'll I meet you?'

'Make it Beehive Place, around six o'clock.'

'Okay.' Leroy Jackson dumped his books behind a radiator, went to the cloakroom, put on his very fashionable knee length leather coat and strolled out of the school gates, past the notice saying 'William Penn Comprehensive', and on to the drab, impersonal streets of East Dulwich. He caught a bus to Electric Avenue, Brixton, and ambled past Beehive Place, past Canterbury Crescent and along to 39a Gresham Road, where he lived.

'That you, Leroy?' came a voice from the dank and peeling interior.

'Yes, Ma,' answered Leroy.

'Police, he come round today.'

'What for he want now?' asked Leroy, worried.

'E want to know who's car it was that been outside for weeks.' Leroy sighed with relief. He had been out 'looking for money' the other night with his friends, and was worried about an old man whom they had 'done' a little too thoroughly and who might have

43

died. There was no feeling for the old man, just worry at the thought of being caught.

'Hey, ma!' he shouted, 'Is my shirt ready for tonight?'

'Yes. It upon de line, outside. You going out tonight?'

'Yeah.'

He collected the shirt from the clothes line and went upstairs to the bedroom he shared with his four brothers. He changed into his best clothes. He then pushed a set of drawers away from the wall, revealing a small hole in the plaster. Leroy pushed his hand into this hole and groped around until his hand closed on a paper bag. This he took out. He emptied the contents – a packet of cigarette papers, something wrapped in tin foil, some tobacco, and a box of matches – on to his bed and sat down next to them. He then took a cigarette paper out of its packet and proceeded to roll a cigarette adding a few crumbs of what was in the tin foil to the tobacco being used. He put the cigarette into his mouth and lit it. He inhaled deeply and with satisfaction as the marijuana began to take effect. He put the paper bag and its contents back into the hole in the wall and replaced the chest of drawers. He flicked the ash off the 'joint' and lay back on his bed.

He heard the front door open and a voice say,

'I'm back, Julie.' His father was back early! 'Leroy home yet?' he continued.

'Yeah.'

'I got something for him.' He started up the stairs. In a panic, Leroy stubbed out the cigarette, opened the window and started fanning the smoke in its direction. The door opened and his father walked in. He opened his mouth as if to say something but stopped, and sniffed. His face contorted with anger.

'You little bastard!' he said, 'You've been smokin' de ganja[1] again.' Leroy wasted no time. He raced out of the room, down the stairs, through the front door and out onto the street. He could smoke ganja when his mother was in the house because she never came up to the room, and in any case, she couldn't beat him up. But his father! He was always coming into the bedroom and he was also as strong as a bull: with a temper like one. He could smoke in safety with his brothers: they were all huge and his father would never dare beat anyone of them. Unfortunately, they were all at work.

He stopped running and looked at the watch he had taken from the old man as he lay prostrate while Leroy's friends kicked him

[1] ganja: West Indian slang for marijuana.

in the head. It was six o'clock. He strolled a short length down Brixton Road and turned into Beehive Place, this was a sort of market but it was enclosed by walls and a glass roof. He stopped by a record stall and looked into the reggae section. Delroy Wilson had a new single out, 'Tighten Up Volume Six' had just been released, all good stuff. He wished he could afford a record player.

'Hey, Leroy.'

'Hi, Clancy.' Leroy looked the smallish coloured boy up and down and gave him the Black Power handshake.

'I hungry,' said Clancy, 'What time Sundown open tonight?'

'Seven.'

'Let's get some food,' Clancy said.

'Where from?'

'Wimpey.'

'I got no money!'

'So what, man, you got legs, eh?' Leroy smiled. He got the meaning. They found their way out of Beehive Place and walked into the nearest Wimpey bar. They sat down and Clancy lit a cigarette. They started talking about reggae, something they both had a deep interest in, until the waiter came to their table.

'Yes?' he said.

'Two Wimpey Cheeseburgers and two cokes, please,' said Clancy. The meal came and they ate hurriedly, in silence.

'C'mon, man,' said Leroy, nervously.

'Not yet!'

'When?'

'Wait 'till the waiter man goes round de corner.' Clancy paused.

'Now!' he whispered. The two youths got up and walked quickly toward the exit.

'Hey you!' The waiter had seen them and was coming after them. The two boys bolted out onto the street and ran as fast as they could along it. The waiter followed them.

'Let's stop in a alley,' panted Leroy.

'What for?'

'The waiter man'll follow us and we do him.' Clancy approved. They dived into a narrow side-street, stopped, and pressed themselves against the wall. The waiter blundered into the trap.

'Now,' hissed Leroy. Quick as a flash, Clancy's foot snaked out and tripped the man up. He fell heavily onto some cardboard boxes. Leroy brought his foot hard to the man's temple. The waiter had got up into a crawling position when Clancy let fly a kick into his groin. The man doubled up and was sick on the pavement. Leroy smashed his heel into the man's mouth as he was rolling around on the floor.

'C'mon,' Clancy said. They both ran off, leaving the waiter semi-conscious. The two youths checked the time to see if it was open yet, and set off towards the Sundown Discotheque.

When they got there, the doors had opened, but there was still a queue. The sound of music wafted out from the domed building. They joined the fast-moving line of people. Leroy looked at his watch: half-past seven. Clancy said approvingly,

'Isn't it nice to see so many of our kind in one place wit' no wasps[1] around?'

'Yeah,' nodded Leroy. The two, once inside, looked around for friends. 'Hey look, der's Paul and Winston!' Leroy shouted to make himself heard above the music. They walked over to where their schoolmates were standing.

'Hello Paul,' Clancy said. Leroy nodded to Winston.

'Hey man,' said Winston excitedly, 'You should 'ave been seen what 'appened just fifteen minutes ago,' he went on, 'I was standin' in dat corner over dere,' he indicated the top left corner of the dance hall, 'when I 'ere dis noise – a commotion, like over dere.' He indicated the bottom right hand corner of the floor. 'I went over to see what happened and I saw these rude boys[2] tearin' de clothes off some wasp-boys.'

'Nice, man,' grinned Leroy, 'What happened?'

'Well de police took care of it, and all 'came calm, like.' Leroy changed the subject to their previous 'bundle with the waiter.' Paul and Winston nodded with approval, as Leroy told the story, interjecting with comments like 'Tasty, man' or 'Juicy.' This mode of conversation, and the music took them through the better part of the evening. At eleven o'clock, however, a series of shouted obscenities, coupled with the sound of breaking glass, coming from the entrance, attracted the boys' attention. They, along with half the people on the dance floor, started drifting towards the commotion. Leroy soon saw the source of the trouble: about fifty or sixty white youths had forced their way through the entrance. One of them shouted, 'Come on you black bastards! Strip us!' As soon as Leroy heard this he charged over to the entrance and hurled himself at the nearest of the whites, who

[1] wasps: slang word meaning whites in general but originally derived from the American White Anglo Saxon Protestant.

[2] rude boy: petty thief; thug; villains – West Indian slang.

were now kicking and punching any black within reach. Leroy smashed his fist into the youth's face and then, as he was trying to protect himself, started kicking him. Leroy grabbed the white's neck and hurled him to the ground where he started aiming kicks to the youth's groin. He doubled up in agony and started screaming. Leroy shouted out, 'Come on, rude boys, hit them hard!' The instruction was not needed for, already, black youths were hurling themselves at the white. Leroy, out of the corner of his eye, saw somebody aiming a kick at him. He turned quickly sideways onto the kick and caught it on his thigh. He grabbed the white by the hair and punched him in the throat. The boy lashed out and hit Leroy on the jaw. That hurt! He tripped the white up and, as he was falling, kicked him full in the face; he felt the nose break, Leroy was just going to throw a fist at another white face when he felt himself being pulled to the ground. He struggled to regain his balance but was clubbed down. Instinctively, Leroy curled up tight to protect himself from kicks that were raining upon him. He felt sharp stabs of pain in his shins, his back, his head. All of a sudden these blows ceased. Leroy felt himself being hauled up. He twisted round and saw a face under a blue cap.

'Okay boy,' said the policeman, 'You comin' quiet?' Leroy struggled but the man was too strong. 'Yeah,' he said, resignedly. The policeman dragged him through a door marked 'exit' and bundled him into a police van. The door slammed shut and Leroy heard it click. After a five-minute drive, the van stopped. The door was opened and a voice said, 'Okay nigger, out.' Leroy's insides tensed and he burned with rage. He'd always thought British police were pretty fair on the whole. He was taken to a charge room and pushed into a seat. A great, thick-set, red-faced policeman came in, sat down and typed something on a yellow piece of paper.

'Sign it,' he ordered, giving the paper to Leroy. It was a statement that read something like this:

'I was in the Sundown Disco, when some white boys came in. Me and my mates started pushing them around and tearing clothes off them. Later, a load more white boys came in and we started on them. The police stopped us and I took part in an identification parade where I was recognized by the boys I had torn clothes off.'

Leroy looked at the bit of paper contemptuously and said slowly and deliberately,

'Piss off, pig. I wasn't doing de tearin of de clothes for I was not dere.'

'What did you call me, nigger? Anyway I saw you down there, pushin' them lads around – and I saw you run when we came along. I got it all in my report and the sarge has got a copy. You're done for, nigger.'

'You can't a' seen me, man, I wasn't dere. Anyway all you pigs are liars – and you stink!' The policeman lost his temper and started hitting Leroy around the head. Presently he went, but was soon back with two replicas of himself. He walked up to Leroy and said menacingly, 'Now are you goin' ter sign it?' Leroy knew he had lost. 'Got no pen,' he said, sullenly. The policeman produced one and grinned at his colleagues. They strolled out of the room, leaving Leroy by himself. Two minutes later, a sergeant walked in with a cup of tea.

'Take sugar, son?' Leroy looked at him in surprise. 'Smoke?' the sergeant continued.

'No thanks and er, two sugars, please,' Leroy said.

'Can I have your address please?' Leroy told him his address. Thirty minutes later his eldest brother came into the room. 'Papa and Ma didn't want to come,' said the brother.

'Suits me,' said Leroy.

'I payin' de bail!'

'Oh, thanks, man,' Leroy said, gratefully. The proceedings for bail went through without any problems. The police let Leroy go. As he was making his way to the door, he saw a man with blood stains on his face and vomit on his clothes being supported by a policeman at the desk. The man pointed at Leroy and started shouting, 'That's one of 'em! I'd know him anywhere!' It was the waiter. Leroy was taken back to the charge room, accompanied by his brother. The same policeman, who had made him sign the statement, came in and said wearily, 'What have you been up to now?' He sat down and went on, 'At seven fifteen you and another boy, done over a waiter from the Wimpey.' Leroy smiled and said cooly, 'No I didn't. How could I? I was tearin' clothes off people's backs, remember?' Leroy got up and stuck his head next to the policeman's and said, 'And who made I sign de thing? I could get you into trouble, man.' The policeman blanched. 'Now you better clear I,' went on Leroy, 'or you know what might 'appen!'

'All right mate,' the policeman was trembling. 'I'll just tell him I got proof that you were somewhere else at the time.' Leroy nodded. 'That'll do pig.' The policeman went out and was back in five minutes. 'Okay mate,' he said, 'You can go now.' Leroy and his brother sauntered out. As he passed the desk he heard,

'It was him, it is him. I'd know him anywhere.' The waiter was still there. Leroy turned to him and said,

'Maybe you made mistake, man. Remember, all us niggers look alike.' Both he and his brother burst out laughing.

In court, two weeks later, Leroy was sentenced to two years probation for disturbing the peace (nothing could be proved about him causing grievous bodily harm). He would have probably been sent to a detention centre if the assault on the waiter had been proved. As he walked out of the court he was grinning. He said to his brother,

'Don't look now, man, but I think I smiling from my arse!'

JES SCHOOLING 15

The New Beginning

He awoke abruptly and stared, stupefied for a moment at the brilliant spring sunshine, infiltrating the disorganised chaos of the small and dingy room, illuminating and rejuvenating even an ancient wardrobe of mammoth proportions and awkwardness. Then his thoughts slipped instinctively back into their familiar waking ruts. He wallowed briefly beneath the warm weight of the bedclothes and his own habitual contented melancholy, then the glorious fact of spring became too much for him and he leapt explosively from the bed, remembering, as his bare feet hit the cold, brown linoleum floor, the promise he had made to himself the day before. He liked to keep his promises, even those made secretly to himself in the middle of the night in a maudlin state of intoxication, for he was a great believer in strength of purpose. This particular promise had been wonderfully plain and simple – nothing more nor less than a fresh start. He had made such promises before, but they had always involved complicated philosophies and intricate plans for daily living, which would break down after a couple of hours of faithful adherence to them. But today would be different.

As he dressed, he pondered over his resolution and realised that the day being Saturday it would be at once easy and difficult to keep. There was no compulsion upon him to arise at an early hour and attend a lecture, on the other hand this very fact was likely to discourage him from working, and today was a day for accomplishing things. He decided that the auspicious occasion must be marked with a symbolic action and carefully searched the room for something befitting its solemnity. Finally after much grave deliberation, he picked upon his boots, which had been cleaned perhaps once in the preceding six months, and were still caked with the mud of that last disastrous riverside encounter. He tried not to think of the events of that afternoon as he scraped the dry, crumbling mud from the boots with a penknife, onto the brown linoleum, swept it tidily under the bed and reached with due ceremony for the unused tin of brown polish which reposed in its untouched virgin splendour between an open jar of marmalade and two congealed sausages on a white enamelled plate. On opening the tin however, he remembered that he possessed no brushes, so after a messy application of polish with his fingers, he shone the boots with an old shaving brush, discarded when he had begun to grow a beard to avoid the loathsome early morning ritual before the mirror.

Tomorrow's breakfast, he resolved, as he sat, distastefully picking and prodding at the cold sausages, would be an altogether more successful affair. The ghastly repast finished he decided that a brisk walk in the first sunshine of the year would be a healthy and profitable activity and would prepare his mind admirably for the intellectual labour he intended to achieve that day. So, having forgotten completely to wash up his breakfast things, he hurried from the dismal surroundings of his room, down a dark uncarpeted staircase and out into the street.

Spring had most certainly arrived. The air was sharp and clean; it had lost its usual, clammy negative quality; golden sunrays pierced the pale faces of people waking bewildered from a long winter's sleep. He could not even feel contempt for them today, for he knew himself to be one of their number. But he would astonish them yet. What did they see, if indeed they even registered his passing? Another tatty student in the toils of deep thoughts? But a student with a purpose, and a reason too, as from today. He lingered beneath a tree to wonder just exactly what that purpose was, for he had refused to define anything for himself today. He concluded that his aim was a complete renovation of his life-style. Work and other assignments would be completed on time, profound opinions would be expressed, and even more important, sweeping conquests would be made of all the college's most desirable females. So absorbed was he in his contemplation of future delights that he failed to notice the mockingly ironic glance bestowed upon him by one of the most remarkable of these examples of feminine perfection, but passed on, his eyes widening in pleasure at the momentous scenes which were occurring with great activity just behind his eyes.

Meditation upon the female sex brought his thoughts spiralling inevitably down to one particular member of its ranks. She of the riverbank. He could not imagine her in any other setting now. He had his one mental picture of her, standing fog drenched and sobbing by the riverside, shoe deep in mud, one sodden auburn curl trailing limply upon her pale forehead from beneath the hood of a tattered grey duffle coat. That was the only way he would ever remember her now, but somewhere in the waking city, she still existed, was perhaps, like him, registering the first day of spring. Perhaps, he thought, as he wandered unnoticing down familiar lanes, perhaps he owed her an apology; today was after all a day for tying up loose ends, for shaking off the shades of the past and for starting anew. He decided against it finally: to see her again would complicate life rather than clear up anything, would weave once more the intricately involved complexities of their relationship. Certain things must be swept beneath the carpet and forgotten when one attempts a new beginning. It was surprising how quickly her image was disappearing from his mind. Did people always forget one another? Why could he remember the face of an uncle who had been dead for five years and not that of the earnest student of philosophy from the room across the landing? Then he remembered in horror the total irrelevance of such idle speculation. One must discipline the mind, just as one should discipline the body. Mental discipline was not something which one could acquire in a day; he knew that, he thought wryly, remembering endless, sleepless nights when restless mind tormented fatigued body with wildly spiralling thoughts and images.

Suddenly he became once more aware of his surroundings. He was in a dark and narrow lane, bordered with leafless trees and high grimy brick walls. The trees were short and squat, they had been indiscriminately lopped so that they were covered with strange, unnaturally bulging growths. The sun had disappeared behind a small grey cloud which seemed rapidly to be increasing in size. He shivered slightly, then remembering that logic and rational thinking were all important, strove to set aside the unreasonable fears which had suddenly beset him.

As he emerged from the alley, he found himself unaccountably thinking of damp, limp auburn curls, and the sun too had relinquished its darkness and blazed forth with golden benevolence. He found that he had walked full circle, as he had done on so many unforgetable occasions before. The sight of the sun reminded him that he had no idea of the hour of the day, and that there was much work awaiting him in his room. The only timepiece he had ever possessed lay backless and without a strap, on the window sill, its works scattered invisibly across the universe, after its use as a weapon in the last great disagreement which had caused the final rift. He was in his own street now, a fairly important street, and there was a clock in a chemist's shop on the other side of the road. Screwing up his eyes to see it better, he failed to notice a small child hopping along the pavement ahead of him. Sudden acceleration caused by horror at the advanced hour, brought him into collision with the bouncing child, knocking a doll from her arms into the muddy gutter. Normally he would have stopped to retrieve the treasure with a kind apology, but it was three o'clock, nothing had been achieved, so he left the child standing there, white faced and half sobbing as he rushed back towards his room.

It was long past dinner time, so he cut himself a piece of cheese with the penknife he had used to scrape the mud from his boots, and opened a bar of chocolate. Then with an increasingly sinking heart, for the day was aging and what had he achieved, he approached the disordered heap of papers on his table. When he finally managed to find the title of an obligatory piece of work, scrawled on a creased and blotted scrap of paper, he realised that he had neither read the necessary works nor attended the necessary lectures, and moreover, the thing should have been completed several weeks previously. What had he been doing for the last three months? There had been so much to do, time was always occupied, but now, looking back he could no longer remember anything but rare and isolated incidents. It could not have taken him so long to find the concealed pathway from the interwoven complexities of the auburn labyrinth. His mind slipped further and further away from the task at hand, and he began unconsciously to decorate a sheet of paper with mystic, magical symbols – five pointed stars within regular pentagons. He leant his hand upon his arms and tried to concentrate his thought upon the dictated topic, but thought became less and less coherent until it faded away altogether and he slept.

When he awoke for the second time on that day of new beginnings it was dark. For a moment he was bewildered, groped before him on the table, then shivered and arose to switch on the light, blinking as he looked around the room, as if seeing it for the first time. One small window, engrimed with dirt, looking out onto the street, soiled off-white walls, huge and clumsy wardrobe, darkly ponderous and menacing in one corner, bed unmade, books and papers strewn everywhere, and standing proudly shining on the scuffed brown linoleum – his symbol and only achievement of the new beginning – his boots, speckled now with crumbs of cheese.

He felt suddenly unutterably lonely. He knew none of the other students in the building, neither the philosophers across the landing, nor the two dedicated physicists from the floor above. When two people have built a universe for themselves, believing their happiness to need no one else, the destruction of that universe, and the return to normality is strange and difficult, even when one believes that one is regaining one's freedom. Was he free now, he wondered, now that he was released and liberated from the tortured fantasy world of her imagination? Did apparent freedom gained merit the pain and loneliness that had been caused? He lay down on the unmade bed and considered the day which had passed. New beginnings had come to nothing, the inward life could never change. The past, instead of being tidily swept beneath the bed, had writhed to the forefront of his mind, bringing with it the old tortuous conflict. He got up, switched off the light and let himself fall back onto the bed. He dared not think of a fresh start tomorrow: all he could see was the white face of the child and the doll lying face down in the gutter where he had knocked it.

JANICE LAURA TAYLOR 16

Going Home

The dust swirled in the lights of the heavy lorry as it trundled along the small track in the dark. The crickets chirped in the darkness and the beams of the lights often caught a flitting butterfly or the Midges. It was a long time since he'd been home, a long time since he'd been in this part of the country at all, him living in the east with his father as he did. His parents had split up years before and his father had moved out east with him. He only remembered the little white house – made of wood – as a child would think of paradise: clear air; bright sun; the creek at the bottom of the garden with the mud and stones under which the crawdads fought. It was an old house built just after the civil war out on the edge of a quiet middle-class town, very religious and very quiet. There used to be fields all around the house, all on one side that is, with the horse farm not so far down the road. He remembered those fields with their dark dusty earth, the green, tall, leafy corn plants standing upright in the ground. There was a wood down at the bottom of the garden with a pony in it; the days they had riding that pony, galloping through the woods bareback and holding tight onto its mane.

He'd only been eight at the time but the memories were lodged in his mind as firmly as his name and age.

As the truck turned off the track and onto the main road, a car shot by them on their left with its glaring headlights dazzling them for a while.

'How far now?' the boy asked, with a distinct, clean cut Eastern accent.

The driver made a rumbling noise in his throat as if about to speak but changed his mind and pointed to a sign they were passing. '12 miles' the sign read and the boy nodded and sat back in his seat and looked at the roof of the cab.

He hadn't seen his mother at her home for all those years. She'd always come to Boston. 'Isn't that strange?' he thought. He felt very strange now going home, that is what he always thought of as his home.

It was July so they'd have corn-on-the-cob for dinner, perhaps a ham with brown sugar sauce and broad beans. There'd be a water melon in the fridge and he could almost hear the whir of the air conditioning and the humidifier.

The lorry hit a stone in the road. It was quite a big stone and it jolted the truck, lifting him off the seat. He bumped back down awkwardly, jolting his neck, sending a tingling sensation down his arm. A crick in the neck was always annoying and he sat there with his head slightly tilted.

He thought of the house again, made of slats of wood painted white, the old wooden porch with its swing seat squeaking in the wind and the chinese bells tinkling as they swayed about. In front of the house he could see across the open clearing, for there were no houses opposite, and about 150 yards away, the cornfields as they sloped gently away. He could see the kids playing ball on the grass on the other side of the road in the dusk light, and wishing he could go out and play but knowing soon his mother would gently tell him it was bed-time. He thought of the creek and the times he had followed the older kids up the mere trickle that it was in summer, hunting crawdads and making them fight. And how in the spring the creek would flood and they could swim in it. He thought, too, of the number of Japanese soldiers he had shot dead in the garden, but had got up and run off shouting, 'You missed!'

He remembered the hours he had spent sitting in the cool basement of the house patiently watching his father do something with his tools, on the lathe or on the forge.

The games they played in that basement, throwing soap powder around on Hallowe'en and sliding down the laundry shute into a hugh pile of linen.

He stopped himself; he felt he was getting too excited. He felt he would be disappointed for he knew his mind had probably made it just that little bit too wonderful.

The truck was coming into the east side of the little town, the rich side, which he was glad of for he could see the whole town this way.

He sat up as he heard the driver grunt in his rustic voice, 'We're here,' and then put his hand into his dusty denim overalls and took out a piece of gum and put it in his toothless mouth. He put his arm on the door and straightened his hand, but had to cock it back as his neck still hurt. They came into town quite fast which added to his feeling of excitement as the corn fields gave way to the tall, rich, majestic houses.

There had been a few changes to them, he noticed. After all he had been gone eight years, but they spoilt the place he felt. The houses had lost their age, for people had put glass porches on the front and the street was bordered by tall, new, electric lamposts. He felt slightly depressed by seeing things had changed at all, even though he knew they would have done.

The lorry slowed down as they came towards the square. He could see the fountain in the middle just as it had been, only it was spotlighted. He frowned; he could sense something else. The lorry turned slowly into the square. It was the same shape as it always had been, with the same roads leading off as they had, but that was the only same thing. There was a cop car to the left and leaning against it was a cop eating a hamburger and holding a can of coke. Apart from that the square was deserted. But the shops! What had they done to the shops!? The old drugstore had disappeared, so had the fire station and there were no houses there. They were all shops, shouting at him with their great glass windows and flashing pink and lime green neon lights.

There were new drugstores, new tailors, new shoe shops, all very modern with their flashing neon lights and big wide glass windows. Behind the cop car was a hamburger joint with music and steam wafting out the door and its hot yellow light pouring out onto the pavement.

He frowned again; he had only been gone eight years. He felt bewildered. Not angry or upset, but bewildered in the way you do when you find paradise is now just as sleezy as anywhere, a childhood paradise as well.

The truck lurched round the square and down West Jefferson Avenue which was a hill, surprisingly as it always had been. The truck had gone through the square too quickly for him to take it all in properly, but he was amazed to see that there were houses everywhere. There used to be spaces, vegetable gardens, dogs that chased you, old allotments of grass. There were only houses now. He wondered if it all looked different because he had his head cocked to one side. How could Eastern living stretch this far?

They crossed the railway tracks by the grain mill and that was like it always was. But next to it was a very plushy 'Drive-In' that had a purple sign that flashed. The truck drove under the railway bridge and up his road. He prayed that it wasn't different. All he could see were houses stretching out in a long line. At the end he could see the school. He knew about the 'High School' being there because his mother had told him about it – but in black brick? Nowhere could he see his house and the fields. Where were the fields?

Suddenly the truck stopped, he wondered why, then he saw his house. The house was the same only it was in the middle of houses – there were no fields in sight. Nowhere! There were houses all around, all new and made of brick, not the nice old wood. He got out of the lorry with his bag and said thank you as the truck rumbled off. He dared not look in the garden and he turned and walked down the gravel drive, newly laid, noticing the automatic in the garage and he rang the bell waiting to see his mother.

DAVID MAXWELL YOUNG 14

Not Allowed

We always played cowboys and Indians,
When we were young,
We always played commandos,
When we were young,
Hiding behind bushes and shooting our enemy.
I thought it was just children who played that.
They're not allowed to now,
Because the grown ups are playing it
But they really die.

MARTA LOUISE MUNRO 15

Dom Cassian

Dom Cassian – what do you think there –
High on the breast of the valley –
Amidst the salt grass and
The whicker's mystic herbs?
Can you breathe so high,
When the spirit of night
Wraps her cloak of oblivion about your
Grey pinnacle of stone?
It must be cold to kneel upon stone slabs
At five, when day breaks the code
That you are bartering your life to learn;
And when you stumble
Through the arched brow door,
Doesn't the carpet of the market place
And the scent of sweet
Melons and lemons
And wheat and breads and corncakes
Make you breathe deep?

Dom Cassian – we float,
Drowning in colours and singing,
Rescued by love and experience:
But you
And your brothers stand
Like fingers on the hill hand palm,

Not waving or beckoning
But clutching, like a man
Caught in quick sand,
Dying without reprieve.

You were born of a seed
Of lust, maybe love;
You survived the undignified
Process of birth,
Through blood and fire membrane,
And effort and pain,
Like I.
You burnt dreams in hot, decaying hay,
And took silver fish
With hands burned brown
From waters stained green
And cried at death,
And cringed from disfigurement
And laughed at the jesters
Like I.

Why, then, do you cringe from warm love,
To cold faith?
Without doubt?
Without loss?
Without question?

Dom Cassian – what of the future?
You cannot trade one cell for a psalm.
Not one heart beat for a blessing.
Nor gold blood for a gospel.
What when the silence of cold
Deafens you?
When your covers no longer
Warm your body?
Will your faith give you shield and shelter?
Will your celibate sceptre
Be substitute for
A tear of love from a baby?
Or a smile from a friend?
Or the sight of your child sleeping?

Dom Cassian – what if God has grown tired?
What if he had died of defeat when he looked
On the wars
And the hate
And the blind eyes?
What if he died of grief for his wildered
Dove of peace?
Who will have the last laugh then?

Dom Cassian – your face grows grey.
There is no horizon
Above your robes to
Your shaded jade eyes.
They are to water.
Is it the quest or
The question?
Dom Cassian – who will have the last laugh, then?

HEATHER CRESSWELL 16

Bless Me Father!

Everything was fine when we left home. It was obvious that, for the moment, my mother had completely forgotten. Even the long, thoughtful bus ride into town did not jog her memory. And, as we left the bus at the bus station, and still she did not remember, the situation began to look very hopeful.

However, as we stood outside the fruit shop surveying the price of apples her memory was suddenly and fully restored.

'Confession,' she announced.

'What?' I said flatly.

'Six weeks!' she exclaimed.

'Mmmm . . .' I murmured.

'C'mon,' she ordered.

Gently, we stole across the tiled floor of the porch, our heels making the holy clicking sound which is so familiar in a church. My mother dipped her finger in the dusty white font, precariously held by a smiling angel. Then, with great reverence and concentration she studied the confession times, which she already knew by heart.

The church was small, brown and stuffy. Situated in the back right hand corner was a little cupboard, the very appearance of which was enough to bring on a chronic attack of claustrophobia. Outside this cupboard was a kneeling queue of aged women crouched over solemn black prayer books and thick brown rosary beads, and old men with white hair, expressionless mouths and world-weary eyes.

We studied them for a few moments. We watched their moving lips and lowered eyes. On the whole they presented an awe-inspiring picture. With some hesitation my mother approached the old lady on the end of the queue; 'Is this the queue for confession?' she hissed inanely. The old lady grunted in reply with a pious nod of her head. My mother knelt down with some relief, and buried her head in fervent prayer.

Kneeling down beside her, I watched her for a few seconds with admiration and incredulity. My eyes then wandered to the colourful and impressive altar. I studied the golden roses, the shining golden candlesticks with their swirling, flickering flames, and the rich purple cloth of the curtain behind the altar. I carefully observed the small, plump priest who knelt with bent head at the altar rails, and with a sigh I closed my eyes and tried to pray.

A sudden stirring in the atmosphere made me open my eyes. A sidelong glance assured me that I now had company. The empty space beside me was now taken up by a tall, stout lady. The first thing that I became acutely aware of was her purple hat, which covered a grave, aggressive face. Her figure was submerged by a large hostile blue coat. I listened to her loud, heavy breathing and bearing her blue coat and purple hat in mind, I realised that I was in the presence of a power far greater than I. So I bit my upper lip, and closing my eyes, prayed earnestly.

The minutes passed, reluctantly, almost begrudgingly, I now knew every detail of the appearance of the church. I knew how many people were waiting in the queue for confession and had guessed which sins they were anxious to confess. I knew the exact rhythm of the heavy breathing of the old lady next to me. My knees had become numb and my hand which clasped my shopping bag had turned a rather nasty shade of purple. This was the result of both the cold winter weather, which always discolours my hands, and the weight of my shopping bag. Suddenly I let go of the bag. It fell to the floor with a bang, but nobody noticed, all were lost in deep meditation. I stared at my purple hand which appeared and felt so lifeless and unfamiliar. I prodded the knuckles and immediately white dots appeared. I watched them fade, as the purple colour flowed over and drowned them. I

60

played around with this ugly purple object for some time, when gradually I became aware that Mrs 'Purple Hat' was watching me with some suspicion. I carried on, pretending not to have noticed. I turned each finger under and then in turn straightened each one, apparently unconcerned with the questioning world around me. Adults tend to worry about my purple hands and I wondered if she thought I had cancer of the hand. The idea of having cancer of the hand appealed to me. Its very name stirred sympathy and interest, and it was so unique, 'practically extinct', I would be able to boast, 'my doctor just thought my hands were cold.'

The queue for confession lessened as more and more people entered the confessional and left, surprisingly enough, alive. Every time somebody left the bench, the whole row shuffled along further up the bench, and I watched with dismay as the bench became shorter and shorter.

Time passed and now my mother was on the end of the bench. The usual nausea overcame me, as I carefully chose out my more presentable sins. A wave of cold, fresh, tingling air splashed against the back of my neck as the church door opened and a crowd of people shuffled in, and stood conspicuously at the back of the church. My turn next!

My fists clenched and my lips tightly pressed together, I mentally walked across the unyielding, brown polished floor to the formidable confessional door. I began to feel very sick.

'It's easy,' I told myself, 'Nothing can go wrong.' I tried to think of trees in winter, my wooly hat, my sister's kitten, my bed on a Saturday morning and the taste of steamed suet pudding. It helped and soon I began to feel moderately confident in a nervous sort of way.

However, an unforeseeable incident took place. My heart sank and I committed my spirit to the Lord, as, aghast, I watched the group of people who had been standing at the back of the church, suddenly surge forwards, and position themselves outside the confessional door. Sadly I wondered if there was anything I could do about it, apart from weeping – or praying.

It was about that moment that I received a violent nudge in the ribs from Mrs 'Purple Hat'. Doubling up in agony I smiled weakly at her.

'Ere, ere, what a t'do, look at d'em,' she whispered with much volume and confusion.

'Ah,' I commented intelligently.

'Ooh, watta t'do, jumping the queue,' she hissed, sounding much the same as the first line in a modern poem.

'Mmmmm,' I said trying to sound furious and indignant.

'They gotta be told,' Mrs 'Purple Hat' firmly announced; and, with these somewhat significant words, she leapt out of the bench and, waving her banner high in the sky, she launched a determined sally on the enemy.

'Us in that kneelers next,' she shrieked in a shrill whisper.

'Pardon?' they asked elegantly, lowering their cold, holy eyes for a second, their voices echoing mightily against the roof of the church. Mrs 'Purple Hat' refused to be disconcerted by their immortal manner and waving her handbag she began her second attack.

'Us in that kneeler; been waiting – our turn now, that young lady!' she screeched, pointing her finger in my direction.

There was a long heavy silence. Then, once again, the invaders condescended to lower their eyes and speak.

'All people waiting to go to confession stand outside the confessional,' they announced caustically. I waited, sure that they would name the year, and exact bill in which Parliament had passed this solid and unarguable fact. However, they did not, but instead assumed a haughty air of dignified silence.

Mrs 'Purple Hat' trembled with rage from the purple berry on the tip of her hat to the shiney brown polish on her clean leather shoes. Her mouth shook with fury as, without any more hesitation, she ran to the little plump priest who knelt motionless at the front of the church. Poking him on the shoulder, until she received his full attention, she heatedly poured out her injustices and complaints.

Seconds later the little priest was on the scene, his very walk suggesting peace and settlement. A master of diplomacy, his methods were simple, he tactfully assured everyone that they had all been right and everyone else wrong, at the same time shrewdly rearranging everybody so that when he had finished everybody was so confused that peace and silence were resumed. I was still next.

We passed by the collection boxes, holy water fonts and local parish magazines. We took a leaflet on prayer and, picking up a pamphlet on St Joseph, we dropped five pence in a polish tin. I closed the porch door behind me, and re-entered the world of innumerable screeching vehicles, putrid streets attacked with litter, and tall ugly cardboard boxes which hide the sky and suddenly I felt very close to God.

PHILOMENA RAFTERY 15

And the Next Morning it was Raining

And the next morning it was raining.
I sat in bed in the half light, half dark,
Hugging my knees to me.
Remembering.
You woke then
And we looked for a moment at each other;
There seemed nothing to say.
Embarrassed
You lit a cigarette,
And I rose and found my dressing gown.
I drew back the curtains:
The sky was empty –
Void.
As were we.

As we silently drank coffee
I wondered how you had replaced the bold poet
Of the night before
And when the change had taken place.
I searched for something to say
Whilst despising you because
You were not he.
But when you had gathered your clothes
And gone,
I cried for the beauty we had briefly known
And so quickly lost.

JULIE RACHEL DICK   14

How did I arrive here?

How did I arrive here?
And these crisp white sheets,
With their shadows and contours,
Hills of pure light and
Valleys of morning blue.
These are not mine.

And these ashtrays are full,
The bottles are empty,
And the clear light pours in on them.

A clock starts ticking and
A confused fly buzzes in a different room.
It is morning
This is a morning in spring.
But why is this not my home or my bed?

It was
Last night,
In some smokey string of events,
I was
Shown here –
Milk bottles chime at the door: I turn my head.
And who is this stranger beside me?

MICHAEL GEORGE TRAYNOR 16

Crucifixion

Why do you nail yourself onto your own cross? Your one un-
hammered hand, the one that you used to fix the nails, is lame
and lonely, hanging limp; it is alien, because it is free and its
friends are dying. So you stretch it upwards into the sky, reaching
out like an imprisoned bird, like a beggar, imploring for help; and
as a final insult you are trying to squeeze vinegar out of the sun.

You are ruining your own picture. This is not what we expected.
So no-one will help you; no-one will even come to look at you.
There will be no loving disciples at your crucifixion. They will
come, and they will turn away. They will come prepared to weep
beautifully and bravely for you, and walk away with their heads
bent, frightened and bewildered, and blame you for planting
disillusionment in their hearts. You see, you are doing it all wrong.
The pain that radiates from your brow is too much for eyes to
bear; like the sun you eclipse, it reflects, and already a small seed
of this you have shown them grows and gnaws inside them. It
hurts, so they run, saying,

'This is not what we wanted to see.'

Then there is you, and me, alone, and silence. So shielding
my eyes from your pain, although I can feel it twisting like a knife,
I will take you down. Pretend my name is Mary-Magdalen or
Virgin, the distinction has no meaning for me, or for you; it is
not a mother you need now, nor a whore. When I am the only
stranger between you and your isolation, and you have lowered
your head in capitulation on your breast, sunk in your own misery,

64

so that your pain no longer belongs to you but lies all around you like a spirit, will you let me lift you down, more tenderly than any healer setting shattered bones?

Gently I will lay you on the grass, and straighten your twisted limbs. Slowly, exquisitely, I will run my lips over your body, drawing our your pain like poison. With grief I will soothe the lines from your brow until only light shines from your eyes; with love I will wash away your suffering, until there is no trace of wounds. In the twilight I will sit beside you, watch over you, and when I have made you pure, and perfect, as you once were, only then will we resurrect the theme. Secure from intruders, for this moment is mine, I will build you a new crucifix; I will do it as it should be done, so that you shine out flawlessly like a deep diamond on the blue velvet cushion of the sky. And when I have placed you there I will kneel below you and look, and look, and drown in the beauty of my vision. For this time there will be symmetry, and grace, and above all, art, and all that you were lacking before I saved you.

And the sun rises, slowly, mutely, wonderfully, to pay its respects to your martyrdom.

I think the real reason I want to crucify you must be because if I do it well enough it becomes the only way in which I can sacrifice you without hurting myself.

SALLY VERONICA PARTINGTON 16

The Uncatchable

The sun came up at about half past five on a day of the summer holidays. I crept out of bed and had a hurried breakfast. The birds had not been singing long when I fastened my fishing basket to my back and tied my two rods onto each side of the crossbar of my bike. I adjusted my basket to a comfortable place on my back and made certain nothing was dangerously dangling in the wheels of my bike, as I had fallen off before due to misadventure with an open rod case. I set off to a fishing place I knew well and I frequently caught nice sized tench and carp. My idea of a nice sized fish is about four to five pounds – I reached the pond at about twenty minutes past six and the pond was covered with a thin mist which rose slowly into the air in long wispy fingers. I padlocked my bike to the old wooden fence which skirted the pond on one side. I expect it used to surround the whole pond to stop cattle from sinking in the deep mud which lay in a barren waste on that side. I climbed the fence carefully as I had nearly fallen into the water the other day when I got my foot stuck in an old rusty hinge. Soon I had my tackle set up with a piece of bread paste on the hook for bait, I was using a six foot rod with nine pound nylon gut bound onto my reel, and a small red tipped float with one lead shot to make it 'cock' in the water. I cast out about five yards, clicked the bailarm over on my reel and sat crouching low on my basket which made a rather uncomfortable seat. The wind rustled the long willow stems and made them ripple the surface of the water. Lilypads bobbed up and down and a moorhen swam noisily past. Now and again a hugh fish would crash onto the surface after leaping from about three feet away. The temptation to cast out to that spot was irritating as I know that some monster from the deep could be just about to take my bait. I sat silently waiting for my float to suddenly wobble or dip sharply in the water, but nothing happened. The sun rose higher in the sky and the sky became a clear blue which made the surface of the water blinding to look at. I could just make out the red tip of my float in the blue-white expanse. Dragonflies flew around my rod tip, blue and green wings flashing in the sunlight, huge crows croaked noisily to one another in an oak tree nearby and I still sat in the shade of a bramble bush watching the red tip of my float. About half past twelve I got up from my seat and rummaged inside the basket to find some sandwiches, I ate them hungrily. Other fishermen had joined me now and they too sat motionless in the glaring sunlight. Some had huge reels and up-to-date equipment and some had small cane fly rods with which they cast with extreme dexterity. Lots of noises filled the air now, the drone of an aircraft, a tractor ploughing the earth in a nearby field, and some noises which were so mingled together I thought it was a man trying to outshout a motorbike. It was a man shouting all right but not about a motorbike, his rod was bent double and a golden shape splashed noisily just in front of a clump of blanket weed. Other men ran to help him with keep nets, wader landing nets and some just shouted instructions. The man battled with the giant fish for half an hour or more and with much skill and bad language he landed the monster safely. It quickly spread around the pond that it was a sixteen pound carp which made my five pounders look a bit sick. The afternoon wore slowly on and my float hadn't so much as wobbled. I cheered myself up by eating some chocolate which I had concealed in my float box, without my Mum nagging on about being extravagent, as I had eaten two bars the previous day. I gazed around the pond and listened to the conversations of other fellow fishermen. The sun slid behind a tree at about five o'clock and no other fish, big or small had been caught. The glare from the water subsided and I could make out the weed banks and other details that I couldn't see before. Suddenly, as I glanced aimlessly at my float, it dipped suddenly and then lay flat on the surface moving slower than a snail on concrete. I gripped my rod with both hands and pushed in the 'check' button. The float dipped and then was gone. I struck hard sideways and I felt a tug as the nylon line twanged taut and the reel strained to turn. A dead weight pulled at my rod and the rod tip bent slowly downwards, men came running, shouting, pointing at me, as I battled with my catch. All noises were blotted out and I seemed to be in a strange noiseless world that was filled with colour. I was bought back to my senses by a sharp pain on my hand. I glanced down to see a raw patch of skin and a broken line off the reel near the bottom joint of my rod. The red tip was in its normal parallel position and the crowd of fishermen had dispersed as fast as they had come, a ring of ever increasing circles disturbed the surface. Evening came and I packed my tackle up and walked to the muddy slippery bank which was always wet whatever the time of year. I climbed the old fence and unlocked my bike. Red patches of the setting sun sparkled through the branches of the trees as I rode off down the peaceful country lane. Tomorrow I would be back in the same place as usual, fishing with a strange keeness that seemed to bring me back day after day. The birds would certainly be there, the strangers, the trees, and the familiar noises will accompany the sudden splashes made by the Uncatchables.

BRIAN JOHN WARNER 14

The Game

They used to play a lot down by the mill. Cowboys and Indians was their favourite game although how they managed to make a tribe out of ten people, I do not know. The mill pond was the water hole where the buffalo came to drink. The stakes at each end of the bridge were their totem poles. I sometimes watched them, crouching hidden in the little thicket of trees by the pond.

There was the vicar's son, a curly fair-haired little boy who

used to come to Sunday School every week; one little boy who
went for a walk with his Grandma every week; Paul had written
on his report 'Paul is a helpful and co-operative member of his
class,' so his mother had informed me one day. I remembered the
rest from seeing them down the meadow, squabbling over who
was going to be goal-keeper in their football games and pushing
each other off of the swings.

'Typical boys,' the caretaker had sighed after he had 'clipped
'em round the ear.'

I made my way down to the mill. It was seven o'clock when I
reached the stile because I heard the church clock strike eight as
it did when it was seven. The lane was overgrown with grass and
weeds and I wandered through it towards the stile. A train
chugged past on the left and the birds swerved away from the
screeching of the wheels on the rusty track. The air wavered in the
dying glint of the sun and then it was peaceful. I hoisted myself
over the stile and thumped down onto the turf. I ambled down
to the thicket and collapsed into the grass. A bird drifted past
overhead, lulling me into a coma.

I never heard them come. Perhaps it was because they were
quieter than usual. It was only when I jerked into consciousness
that my eyes focused on the huddled group squatting by the
thicket. It was half light and as they stood up I shrank back.
Their faces were contorted and their hideous images were reflected
in the pool. Their whole bodies seemed to be disfigured as they
slunk back out of sight behind the trees. I lay clamped to the
ground and the dark silence submerged me. Suddenly I heard
a soft padding. It was one of the boys I had seen down the
meadows. He glanced round suspiciously, saw nothing, and
carefully sat down on the grass. A few minutes went past and he
looked around slowly, as if bewildered.

Then I caught sight of them. Three pairs of eyes were staring,
unblinkingly at the boy. They seemed to hang suspended in space
and the silence. I wanted to scream, shout, anything to interrupt
that terrifying silence. I tried to move my cramped limbs but
something almost like fascination kept me hugging the ground.
I shuddered and quickly glanced up without moving my head.
Now there were twelve specks of light glinting against the blackness of the trees. The circle around the boy seemed to have
contracted, the eyes marking points in the circles.

I could feel my body pulsating against the static reality of the
ground. My lips felt dry and cracked against my tongue. The boy

was uneasy now. He shifted round so that now he was facing the pond. He was sucking hard at his thumb.

Then there were more pin-points of light. I could not count them. They were a blur on my eyes. They were much more compact now – like a ring contracting. I wanted to move – I swear I did – but my muscles had lost the power to contract, the ring, contract, muscles. My thoughts were contorted, hideous images were reflected in my mind. The boy made to turn again.

Then the eyes were incorporated in a mass of writhing flesh which surged onto him. I heard him scream.

'I didn't mean t'a tell. Hones'. . . .' His words choked into spluttering. He was forced under four times. A pulsating pulp of limbs and bodies. Their faces gaped like chasms as they heaved over him. Suddenly they were a circle again. I saw his face. He was sucking his thumb when the water sucked him back.

They used to play a lot down by the mill. Cowboys and Indians was their favourite game.

MAUREEN JOY FLITTON 14

Old Age

I had thought old age
Was a happy summer evening,
With the western sky on fire
And little drops of gold
Seeping through the trees,
A little, thatched cottage,
In a dell of green and brown,
An oak-timbered tavern
And happy laughter.

It is not.
It is a wet pavement
And a dirty, terraced row,
A damp, stinking room
And a newspapered floor,
A bench by a telephone-box,
And standing blue veins,
A half-heard threat,
And a fear of the end.

DAVID JARDINE-SMITH 16

69

A Prodigy for the Fool

(in the beginning)
The days turned, as the seasons turned,
The hours melted, and the decades burned,
And all was still,
At the will of the universe,
Motionless, transparent in thought, alone in what oblivion
had brought,
Prescribed a world, so small, so lost, built a structure
at little cost.
Floating around in a vacuum of birth, freeing the parallels
of galaxies between,
Struggling within in a womb of fire.
A throne without a King or Queen, such was this
molten empire.
And it angered, and it raged, as it's flames burnt the
sky,
Until it was spoken in the echoes, and the clouds
began to cry.
Down, down on the dust, that wonders formed,
A shape of dimension, a miracle re-born.

Marvel upon marvel prevailed so soon,
Liquid of eternity, A banished moon,
To guard the night when darkness falls, but none
can hear its despairing calls.

Rocks of strength could not satisfy the hunger
Of the pattern of stars, of a life more further.
Into the technical method of creation,
Now a relation, of the unknown.
And so it was that the water breathed.
It grew, and it grew,
Until life itself knew.
Something had begun, a battle for survival,
Neither lost nor won,
An opponent without a revival.

Soon an ocean without a sea,
Covered the already awakened land.
Out of the mist of the first day dawning
Came man.

A prodigy for the fool,
Was the command from the pool,
That rippled on the edges of silent minds, thirsting
for inspiration with ideas, so blind,
Praying to the stars, sun, and moon,
Gazing into themselves, gazing into the room, made
of words that should never be heard.
Did they care, what lay hidden there,
Trapped within the darkness and gloom?

Strange creatures these, who walked the secret road.
Lights are their ignorance, a shepherd without a fold.
But they touched the walls, where the wind begins.
They freed a life of countless years.
Enslaved their souls with a million sins,
But they will pay for this murder, with sorrow and
tears.

Who would repair the damage, already done?
A word from heaven, a son of man.
But, Jesus Christ, was nailed to a tree.
Who'll take the blame? Neither you nor me!
We weren't there to settle his fate,
Although we stained his name, with blood and hate,
As much as those who stood in the sand, outside
of the walls of the promised land.

Man built, man demolished.
Man created, man abolished.
He was the fool, who stood alone, and lived his
life in methods of his own.
He encouraged war and destruction
While claiming for peace and holy sanction,
Making a church of wood and stone,
Not noticing that the prayers, from the gold had gone.
But they were to be found in the hovels of the
poor, who came to civilisation with nothing.
They only ask for a little more
Of what the lords of wealth call something, which
makes their houses gleam in the sun, their faces shine
with pleasure and pride.

But when the star sets over the hill, their mansions
are barren and cold inside.
Where is the warmth, the warmth to be found?
Is it here, or is it there, or far beyond?
Where was the smile, on the jester's face
When he found that a soldier, was to take his place?

Who is the prodigy, a knowledge so young,
Trained in battle, when time began?
A child of the universe, seed of the stars,
Was it ever meant to be ours?
Was it for the genius, ever to say
We live for tomorrow, but die today?

GLYN RORY WILLIAMS 16

The Pen

The play opens with the stage not too brightly lit and a small girl standing in the centre. She is an angelic looking child, the type which would make the audience go 'Ah! isn't she sweet.' *Nervously she sings this song to a sweet little tune:*

> I wish I were a Daffodil,
> Hay daffy dum come dilly.
> I'd wear a pair of purple socks,
> Now wouldn't that be silly.
>
> I wish I were a Forget-me-not,
> Then you would not forget me,
> But I am not a Forget-me-not
> Because you will not let me.
>
> If I could be a Daisy,
> Hay Daisy dumdy didy.
> I'd swallow a dice, and two brown mice,
> So they could live inside me.
>
> And if I were a Buttercup
> Sing, bundy rundy tundy,
> I'd go to bed and not get up,
> Until a week on Monday.

At this point lights suddenly start to flash and a man dressed completely in black runs on to the stage screaming and waving a large knife. He runs up to the child and, shouting 'I am the Pen, I am the Pen!', *brutally slays her on the spot!*

She falls dead and the stage goes dark. A single spotlight picks out the killer as he wipes the blood off his knife. He says, trembling at first:

PEN: Yes, I am the Pen, and I have killed her, crossed her out. (*Pause*) You didn't like that did you? I have murdered a child, you didn't like it did you?

Would you like me to tell you who sent me, sent me to do this? I'll tell you if you want. It was the writer. Yes, the writer, the author of this play sent me to kill a little girl, and do you know why? I'll tell you that if you want. It was because he wanted you to realize how much you felt for her. (*Calming down a little.*)

You see he was told to write a play. Well he started off with an idea, that idea, but he got so far and then had to scrap the whole thing. It wouldn't come right so he crossed it out with his pen.

He thought a bit more and then had another idea. However this one didn't work out either and he crossed it out in the same way. This happened several times, well you know how it is when you can't think, sitting up till two with cups of coffee and a waste paper bin full of failures. So he gave up and went to bed.

Anyway when he came down the next morning he saw the congealed coffee and the ideas which he had crossed out. Memories flashed into his mind of the people he had invented. That was more than just print in the bin it was people, characters. He had killed souls. Nobody was going to hang him for murder obviously, no-one wants to avenge the death of a piece of paper. But when you have become involved with a fictitious character you do feel for him. We all cheer the 'goody' and boo the bad guy. But these are only the final characters, you wouldn't feel for the crossed out ideas because they were just pieces of paper with a line through them. You've come along to day to see a play and if we were just to hand you out scripts you would be disappointed,

73

and if we were to destroy those scripts you wouldn't care. You wouldn't give a damn about crossed out words. But suppose if the writer were to cross them out at a later stage, suppose if he were to kill real people, then you would care. So he has sent me, his Pen, to destroy people so that you may realise what he was really doing when he crossed out those ideas.

By this time the Pen has moved to one side of the stage. The stage is still dark but at this point the lights come on. In the centre of the stage is a park bench with a young man sitting on it. He is a labourer with a heavy coat and a gas mask case with his lunch in. A young girl of the same age comes and sits on the opposite end of the seat, she puts down a guitar that she is carrying. Both ignore each other at first but then the girl says:

GIRL: I haven't seen you here before.

MAN: Er what, pardon?

GIRL: I haven't seen you here before . . . I've just been to the museum.

MAN: I'm sorry?

GIRL: I've just been to the museum.

MAN: Oh have you?

GIRL: (*Pause*) No, er, not really.

MAN: Oh (*puzzled*).

GIRL: I'd like to go though.

MAN: Oh er, would you?

GIRL: No.

MAN: Oh er what did . . .

GIRL: What made me say I did? Is that what you're going to ask? I don't know really. (*Pause*) What's your name?

MAN: Peter, Peter Thompson, why?

GIRL: Mine's Annabella. What a name! My mother always used to say it sounded like a biological term. The hepatic, the antenna, lumbar and the Annabella. (*Pause*) Peter, do you mind if I talk? To you that is. I'm sorry you do, don't you? I can tell.

MAN: No I don't mind at all. (*There is a few seconds silence.*)

GIRL: Annabella hey. Annabella, region of the stomach close to the Cardiac, adjective annabellic, plural Annabellae, hence belly. (*Said as if reading from a dictionary.*) What a name.

MAN:	I quite like it, no really, we had a cat once called Annabell.
GIRL:	Oh! I'm sorry (*troubled*), oh I really am sorry. I've done it again, I'm always saying the wrong thing and offending people, I'm very sorry.
MAN:	I was just saying that to make you feel better, you've not offended me.
GIRL:	So you don't like it?!
MAN:	Yes but, well, only if you do, I mean, oh anyway you wanted to talk.
GIRL:	Not if you don't want to, I don't want to bother you, I'm always bothering people.
MAN:	It's no bother honestly.
GIRL:	You sure?
MAN:	Yes, now what were you saying about the museum?
GIRL:	That was nothing, you see I left home, no! I mean I just wanted to start a conversation.
MAN:	You've left home! People will be worrying about you.
GIRL:	Oh no, they won't, you see I'm pregnant. (*Pause*) No! No! I'm not pregnant, I don't know what made me say that, I'm sorry.
MAN:	You're worried.
GIRL:	Yeah, that's right, I'm just worried, I just want to talk. What I said at first about museums, I just wanted to talk. I said I hadn't seen you here before when I've never been to this park in my life. I have to talk. I mean, I know there are organisations but I need a person, not a group of professionals, I know they mean well, but it's hard to walk into a building where the people know exactly what to do and say. It's not real.

I want a person, I've tried on three benches today and you're the first. What I mean is we all need something or somebody to hang on to. With some it's a teddy bear or a photograph, or a pebble which they picked up on an enjoyable holiday; or a mirror, no! not a mirror, never resort to a mirror. (*Pause*) You see when I left home I didn't realize. I thought I was just leaving a building which depressed me, a mere square of bricks. But now, now I see I was leaving all my friends and my security, everything I had to hang on to. (*Long pause.*)

MAN: I . . . (*Very touched.*)

GIRL: No, don't say anything. (*She picks up her guitar and says, less sadly than before*), My real name's Susan, I lied there as well, I'm sorry. (*She plucks each string one by one and making no attempt at a tune sings*):

I am Suzey,
Kiss-me-quick Suzey
Then Pass-me-on Suzey
Would you like to love me?

Many say yes,
But I know they mean no,
But I follow them 'cause I've nowhere to . . .

The man takes her hand from the fret board and holds it, she looks at him tearfully. At this point the Pen rushes on stage waving a pistol. 'Oh my Christ!' he shouts, 'No wonder he scrapped this one!' He pushes the bench over sending the two to the ground. He picks up the girl and smashes her across the head with his gun. She falls and he shoots her twice. The man rushes for the Pen but he too is shot.

PEN: No wonder! I mean you see it so many times. It started off O.K. but then dived into the old 'Play for Today' routine. I mean give them two more scenes and they'd be in bed, it never fails!
Do you see what I'm getting at? I had to cross them out, they were winning your sympathy with such trash. I did right to kill them. Now the author has realized what he is dealing with I have power, power to kill what *you* feel for. Only then will you realize the difference between script and actor. (*He leaves.*)

Two spotlights pick out two characters on either side of a dark stage, a Man and a Woman. They are having an argument.

MAN: I'm not going to!

WOMAN: But you must.

MAN: Why should I be treated like some inferior creature? I'm not going to be told, pushed about by a bloke who reckons he's God just because he's got a few more bits of paper than me. Why should I?

WOMAN: But you're just disobeying for the sake of it.

MAN: So what if I am, so what if I am? Why should I be

one of a mass, flies which hang around a carcass that hums as much as they do? It's no good, I know where I'm going, God do you think I haven't thought about it?

WOMAN: It does no-one any good to be different just to spite somebody else. All the rest can see that, why can't you? They've got some sense.

MAN: Sense! Ha, don't give me that, they know nothing, just like flies. They are so indoctrinated with his arrogance that they've become indoctrinated, I mean confused. No wonder they dart around like flies, they haven't chosen anything to stick to whereas I have. I don't have to follow that ponce with his certificates. I'm going to stand by my convictions not his.

(*Sings*)   He who would valiant be,
Gainst all disaster
Let him in constancy follow the Master

WOMAN: There you are, 'follow the Master.'
MAN: Yes but my Master, not everybody else's.
WOMAN: But can't you see that there's no hope for you if your belief goes against everybody else. They are not confused, they've just chosen a safe path.

MAN: The safe path! They just follow each other, like flies as I said.

I am a fly, of a million eyes,
Grouped in two goblets,
Like gazing through cut glass,
A million images dazzle my mind.
I can't follow all of them,
I'm really quite blind.

WOMAN: Your fancy poems will do you no good if you won't conform. If you go out on your own you won't be able to quote verse at people.

MAN: I was only explaining myself. Besides, who says I won't, I'll do as I like, it's a free world isn't it? That's what everybody's been trying to tell me for the whole of my life.

WOMAN: It is, but not when you're on your own.

MAN: Well if you can't be individual it's not a free world is it?

WOMAN: Well no . . .

MAN: Well then. (*Pause.*)

WOMAN: Well have you tried to think why you feel so strongly about it? (*More diplomatic*)

MAN: Yes I've thought, I just do that's all. Haven't I got a right to be determined?

WOMAN: Oh come off it. If they were going to throw you to the lions you'd give in just like that, you're no martyr.

MAN: That's typical, that is! Not an ounce of understanding, maybe I am a martyr.

WOMAN: You're just being childish.

MAN: Maybe I am a martyr, maybe I'm saving people from being imprisoned in a rut. Perhaps it is a religion with me. Maybe my determination is deeper than even I think.

WOMAN: Oh! don't be so stupid!

MAN: Yes,   He who would valiant be,
                 Gainst all disaster,
                 Let him in constancy
                 Follow the Master
                 There's no discouragement
                 Shall make him once relent
                 For his a vowed intent
                 To be a . . .

Here, from the woman's side of the stage the Pen's voice is heard singing Fight the Good Fight. He pushes the woman out of her beam and then the stage becomes lit. He goes over to the man and beats him up. 'You arrogant great oaf, there's nothing original about you. I doubt if they are worried so much about the end of this idea,' *he says and leaves.*

The next scene starts straight away with the sound of music hall laughter coming from off stage. Two clowns run on and music hall music starts.

1ST CLOWN: I say, I say, I say.

2ND CLOWN: What do you say?

IST:	What's green and hairy and goes up and down?
2ND:	I don't know, what is green and hairy and goes up and down?
IST:	A gooseberry in a lift!
BOTH:	Ho ho ho ho ho ho ho ho ho ho ho ho ho ho ho howw *(in the old music hall* ho ho ho ho ho ho ho ho *style)* ho ho ho ho ho ho ho howw
2ND:	I say, I say, I say!
IST:	What do you say?
2ND:	Why do hens lay eggs?
IST:	I don't know, why do hens lay eggs?
2ND:	Because if they dropped them they would break.
BOTH:	Ho ho ho ho ho ho ho ho ho ho ho ho ho howw etc.

Enter a third clown with a custard pie.

3RD:	Oh Mr Jones.
IST:	Yes Mr Bones?
3RD:	I have a present for you.
IST:	A present for me, what can it be?
3RD:	It's a pie.
IST:	Why thank you Mr Bones, may I have it?
3RD:	Why certainly Mr Jones. (*Predictably smashes it in 1st clown's face.*) There you are!
ALL:	Ho ho ho ho ho ho ho ho ho ho ho ho ho ho ho howw etc.
2ND:	I say, I say, I say!
3RD:	What do you say?
2ND:	What did the big bucket say to the small bucket?
3RD:	I don't know, what did he say?
2ND:	You look a little pale!
ALL:	Ho ho ho ho ho ho ho ho ho ho ho ho ho howw etc.
3RD:	Oh Mr C.
2ND:	Yes Mr B.
3RD:	I can't let you get away with that. (*Picks up a bucket.*)
2ND:	Oh no! (*He runs down into the audience followed by the 3rd clown with the bucket. The 2nd clown ducks as the 3rd throws the bucket at him and bits of paper fly all over the audience. Both climb back on the stage and*

the 3rd's trousers fall down as he does so, the music is still going on.)

IST: All right you two, what did the big chimney say to the little chimney?

BOTH
OTHERS: You're too young to smoke!

IST: Dash it, you know it. (*At this point about ten or more clowns run on throwing pies, etc. Then after a few seconds, about fifteen more come on and there is a great corny commotion. They all begin to sing.*)

ALL: Them bones, them bones, them dry bones
Them bones, them bones, them dry bones, etc.

Now enters the Pen firing a large machine-gun, he mows them all down in a heap of screaming gore. The stage goes dark and once again he is in spotlight.

PEN: And so this is the end of the play. (*He walks over to the side of the stage and throws on to the heap of dead clowns the appropriate bodies as he says*) I have killed the meek child, the arrogant, the lonely girl and the one she tried to talk to, the happy. They are all bodies around me now. (*Walks to the centre of the stage.*)

I have ended up with total power; the writer's power maybe, but I am the instrument he uses when he crosses out these people. So if you look at what I have massacred you can see that as regards the play I am the powerful one. (*From out of the darkness on the stage comes a voice.*)

VOICE: You can't kill me.

PEN: Who dared to say that? (*Brandishes his gun.*)

VOICE: You can't shoot me, your power is not supreme because I have the final say.

PEN: Who are you, another idea? I am the powerful one, who are you? (*The lights come on and there is a figure dressed in red.*)

RED PEN: You can't kill me, I am the one who has the final say.

PEN: I was sent by the writer.

RED PEN: I was sent by the tutor.

PEN: Who?

RED PEN: The teacher, I am the teacher's red pen, the one who marks this play. I was sent by the teacher, the one

80

who taught your writer how to create such characters in the first place. So now the tutor has to say what he thinks of all this. (*Points to the bodies.*)

Pen panicking tries to shoot the Red Pen but it has no effect. The Red Pen draws a pistol and shoots him once and in dismay he falls. The Red Pen turns to the audience and says,

RED PEN: So what do I do now, I have any course of action between A+ and E−. Or if I am not quite sure what to make of it I can always put that non-committing tick in the corner. (*Paces out the shape of a tick on the floor.*) Well, what is it to be? I mean it's O.K. but, well it, I mean it was original but . . . Oh I don't know, I'm just one person's pen and it will take all of yours to give it a fair mark. I'd rather leave it to you but I've got to put something. Oh, 'Good try.' (*Paces out the tick.*) Best not give him any more, he may get carried away like that Pen did. (*Leaves.*)

STEPHEN DAVID HEPWORTH 15

Nimrod

Today it is unfashionable to believe in the supernatural. We live in an era of science. Everything can be explained – we are addicted to explanation and to the explicable. Strange happenings are caused, we cynically say, by intoxication or the tendency of yokels to add to their stories. A seal can easily be seen as a mermaid, a steam engine as a dragon. They who have seen ghosts, who have witnessed strange occurrences are drunk, deranged or dreaming. But some things cannot be explained.

. . . . .

Near Chester, lies the little village of Burton. It is a church-clock-at-ten-to-three hamlet, where a sandstone church, antlered with turreted tower, sleeps on a grassy slope above the village – a pleasant muddle of thatched cottages and half-timbered farms.

Down to the shore meanders a road, a yellow ribbon severing white oceans on the map. It swerves to the right on the edge of marsh like a fairground ghost-train. From this tarmacked stream rise red and ancient cliffs, mutilated by deep quarries, rearing up as only cliffs can rear. This is Burton Point. Above, on these sea-cliffs' lofty crown, graze sheep, tearing the grass with all the relentless ferocity of four-footed lawnmowers. Heads bob on white eiderdowned chassis, with little eyes, giving an impression of Tibetan sagacity and a Dali Lama's wisdom. They roam about their grassy fields no doubt ignorant of the fact that where they stand was once a burh, an ancient hill-fort. Here men once fought and charged, killed and died. Here, amongst these slender trees where herons squawk and sing, splitting ears by the dozen, the clash of sword and spear, the shouts of men and terrified screams of horses whirled in bellicose echoes. The sheep graze on regardless.

Before us now stretch acres of pancake-flat land which man has captured from the hungry waves of the river Dee. Here men now farm the pleasant land with undulating wheat and bleating sheep. But once here docked vessels, laden with exotic wine and silks, from far-off Gascony, Britanny and Aquitaine. The dockers bore the crates and casks up the road to waiting carts and ponderous-bellied merchants smiled with greed as the golden coins flooded in. Here once, also, ships of a more belligerent breed moored to carry soldiers to a troubled Ireland and crush her rebels in their moors and bogs. But the Dee, like a sullen sulky child withheld his waters from Burton's sandstone quays, leasing the land to the treacherous salt-marsh, waiting to trap the unwary with his bogs and quicksand. Now the marsh also has packed his bags and departed (by train, no doubt) for Neston and Parkgate nearby.

Before the marsh vanished to a more favourable clime, there lived, on its very banks, a strange old man by the name of Black Jake. He had made his home in the ruins of a railway-station, for the railway snaked along the flank of this reed-carpeted marsh. His living room was the waiting room and he slept amongst the wooden sleepers they had heaped there when they had dismantled the old goods-sidings. He cooked his dinner in the booking-office and kept his pantry on the station name-board wherefrom dangled the feather-strewn carcasses of the birds he had caught on the marsh.

He was indeed a strange old man. His face was hideous, blighted by a fishing accident and drenched with scars. His yellow skin showed through his filthy rags and his one eye stared at one without focusing – the eye of a madman. He hated the world and the world hated him. He lived perpetually alone and talked to no-one but himself, for he had not seen a soul for a gaggle of years.

His home was ramshackle and as decayed as a neglected tombstone. The wind had carved a myriad holes from his roof in many a fit of lupine savagery. The rain torpedoed streams of water through them with a cunning that could not even be forestalled by a galaxy of dull-grey buckets dotted about the floor at strategic points. The walls too were in the rapid process of soliflucting upon the floor. Here and there they bulged in painted crags, while elsewhere, they gaped in caves to the outside world. A door squeaked in sickly tones when the wind crept round the hovel, a door that hung like a wooden corpse from only one hinge. The door opened out on to the embankment that had already begun to cascade down from the ravages of the weather. Down to the marsh twisted a path drenched in a brown clay, whipped into such a viscid sludge that it was indistinguishable from butterscotch blancmange. Sprouted in this semi-liquid mud was a low jungle of dishevelled and untidy vegetables struggling to survive against wind, rain and the voracious sabre-cuts of a pair of neglected goats. The path led to a wooden wharf, next to which nestled a small boat, motionless on the stagnant grey-green water.

Who was this strange old man? No-one knew. Even his name was bestowed upon him by the traditions of Burton village – Black Jake, the Devil's captain. At night, they said, he rode with his horned master in a coal-black sleigh, through the black storm-clouds far above the marsh – before them, galloping the red Yell-Hounds, the souls of unbaptised children. The forked tails of these phantom monsters waved like oak-trees in the wind, and their eyes were as yellow as Sodium lights. After lost souls they galloped, like horsemen in the frenzied pursuit of a fox. The men and women of Burton whispered the hermit's name with the terrified awe of young children, hearts pulsating and stole a glance through the kitchen window to make sure Burton church still gazed, a sandstone Leviathan, above the village. They said he stole children at night and used them to light his fires and frightened their offspring to bed with tales of his awful appearances at night when he hungrily devoured children, bed, blankets and all.

He lived a strange, strange life. Most times he sat on his doorstep, watching the marsh water swirl and bubble and, at night, the blue methane whirl and spiral in spectral ribbons from the rotting expanse. He sang to himself and muttered drivel in long insane chains like a line of elephants at a circus, rocking his head and waving his filthy, luxuriant beard as if it was a long green strand of seaweed. He hunted the iridescent geese in the gullies of the marsh, geese that milled and circled, squawking cacophonously above. And he caught many, for he was an expert shot with his ancient musket and one eye, like Nimrod, the mighty hunter whom the Reverend echoed in the long lists of Noah's begotten, like Physics formulae, in Burton church. Often the crack of rifle-fire would trample and devour the silence in the marsh, and dissolve the green, rippling plain of geese into squawking fragments as a stone creates jagged continents from silvery ice. Black speckles against the grey iron-wool they would spiral, up and always up, and then some would jerk downward, marshward, to land in some stinking fen, and to end its existance as a black charred carcass on Jake's table.

Far out in the marsh, over the waving reeds and the mud-layered pools was the forgotten hulk of a coaster. Many years before, a great storm had grabbed it in its turbulent fingers and, like a spoiled child, flung it on to a low mudbank. Like a stranded whale it lay, its wooden skin splattered over its resting-place as if Esquimaux had stripped it for its meat. Its masts were battered trunks, sweeping their long webs of rigging over the deck like a veil. It lay on its side, like some saurian monster, mournfully chewing the marsh reeds that swept its jagged sides and dreaming of better days.

Only Jake knew how to reach the slumbering wreck; only he could navigate through the winding channels that formed a puzzle as unfathomable as the twisted branches of an oak. And often he would row through the marsh, through mud-sided hollows dug by the sea, to the grey hide and the battered wreck. For a great treasure lay on the mudbank – crate upon crate of beer. He would sit down on the bank and get drunk and then stumbled over the marsh, singing his insane chants. About him swirled the black darkness and the grey, amorphous fog. His wild mutterings drifted in eerie nebulae to the Red Cat, the little red inn nestled in Burton, where men looked warily over their glasses and decided to hurry home before the clock struck twelve and the boggarts emerged on their nocturnal haunts. Through the fens he would splash, stumbling shakily like a cumbersome and inefficient robot with springs for legs, and then scramble up the embankment to his home. Sometimes the night-express would thunder past, like a blue caterpillar with wheels, as at home in scurrying across the green surface of a leaf, as in clickety-clacketing along its metallic river. He would wave his fist at the train and totter on a young calf's legs, screaming abuse at the passangers who shivered with repulsion at the yellow-skinned ranting madman, prancing ghoul-like on the mud . . . mad, indeed, was Black Jake.

The autumn fell. From the sky came flock upon flock of green specks, wheeling in a myriad 'V's against the grey sky, and dropping down to winter on the marsh. The greenery sprouted more and more geese, until the wild carr was alive – and squawking. Jake watched the flocks congregate for all the world as if the marsh was a gigantic airport and plotted their destruction. He looked longingly at his rifle, resting behind him on the station platform and at his boat anchored below him, but he knew that he must wait.

Above circled Ra, the great green bird and his squawking flock about him. It had been a tiring journey from the north. Day after day they had skimmed over the glistening brine and night after night they roosted in the scarred rocky faces of fiord cliffs or on the finger-like forms of granite-white lighthouses like luminous volcanos jutting from clusters of stone in the wild sea. When they had left Denmark and its marshes behind, Ra had not been in command. His place was taken by Gna.

He remembered Gna's fall from power. How he and Gna had battled far above the raging waves. How he was quicker than the old bird – quicker of eye and quicker of movement – and how a dead corpse had plumetted, like a sack of potatoes, down into the waves. Gna was dead and Ra, the all-powerful, the invincible, was in command.

He gave the signal to land. They swooped down. Ra perched, motionless on a protruding rock, and watched his geese grazing amongst the reeds and mud. Yes he was in command – and omnipotent, as he firmly believed. He knew the legends the Men held about him, that he was a god and a demon in disguise – and to shoot him was to incur the wrath of Hell. He led a charmed life. When the Men saw the red tuft of feather emblazoned like a coat-of-arms upon his chest, they knew that this was Ra, and to injure Ra was death indeed. The great bird often saw the look of fear upon the faces of the Men when they saw him, how they made strange signs with their fingers and scurried from him like mice – and it pleased him. He threw back his chest, and let a scream of defiance and of power cut the silence like a sabre.

. . . . . .

November fell and encircled the world with fog and gloom like a grey-scaled python. Rain fell on Burton and ran in torrents down the streets. Puddles stared dismally from the tarmac, reflecting the world like dingy mirrors. The leafless trees stood, tall and stark like tombstones in memoriam of a dead world and the red town hall huddled sulkily in its green copse, its flag hanging limply like potato-peel. The Saturday shoppers scurried through the rain in black silhouettes with mournful faces, over-shadowed by the mushroom-forms of umbrellas. The 'buses slunk through the rain, scraping their blue bodies over the road, and ruminating on their mournful plight in deep, seemingly subterranean rumbles. The shops showed dismal faces to the street. And high above the town the grey clouds shifted and fused into each other in amazing contortions, disgorging perpetual bucket-loads of grey rain on to the world below.

The great python curled down to the marsh and spread gloom and rain clouds there. The rain splashed on to the dirty pools and dribbled down the clay cliffs.

The geese shrieked and screamed into the howling wind and Black Jake knew that the time had come.

He decorated himself in a ragged cloak and took his musket. Down to the cliff he scrambled, the clay springing on to his feet and clinging on like glue. Out over the marsh, he rowed, the boat snaking round the low mud islands, head-dressed with reeds and crocodile-like. Ra watched his batallions rise into the air as they saw the old man fingering his rifle with zeal. They speckled the sky like raisins in a steam-pudding. But he, Ra, did not flee for he knew he was invincible and the Curse still held strong. He stood on his rocky throne and eyed his hunter with arrogant scorn.

But Jake did not stop and hurry home like others who had hunted. A smile lit up his ghastly yellow face with the eagerness of a tiger, prowling in the jungles of night. He aimed his rifle.

It was then that the horrible realisation that Jake was intent upon his death fell upon Ra. He soared into the air – but he was too late. The green bird, emperor of a vast bird population, died, like the warrior he was, in battle. Jake stuffed him away and rowed home. The tide seemed to fight against him with unusual ferocity, and the whirlpools swirled like a fistful of snakes and with a force so angry as to content even their mother, Charybidis, waiting restlessly for unwary sailors in her Italian strait. And as Jake flung the sack over the station-board, black figures seemed to flicker like candlelight in the marsh, strange amorphous phantoms . . . coming nearer, nearer, nearer all the time . . .

.   .   .   .   .

They found him next day at dawn. He must have stumbled crazily all night into the wild forest of tall pines that bewigged the steep hill above Burton. His body was mangled and black and upon his face was a look of horror such as can only be imagined in one's wildest dreams. They buried him in the rain, still dismally hammering on the village. Now his grave is untended and over it luxuriate green, pin-pronged nettles. His tombstone sprawls on a crazy angle and bears an inscription weathered into illegibility. No-one cares for Black Jake.

They say in the comfortable safety of the Red Cat that Barbasan, the devil, had devoured him. Jake had killed Ra and the devil had a bargain to fulfill, a Curse to remember. They say – reluctantly – that on November nights, a weird cry percolates from the bowels of the earth as Ra gets his revenge on his murderer and that weird shapes skip in crazy dances over the marsh. Only the rain knows.

All the strange tales can be dismissed. But some things cannot be explained. Was it just coincidence that Black Jake died after Ra perished? Are the stories they tell nonsense? Or . . .

ANDREW JOHN KEEDWELL 14

A Miner's Wife

He kisses her fat lips
and waves goodbye, his mates in
the cage go with him.
As does hope.

The dirt stains the tin bath
and for this she is thankful
to God who gave her memories,
and now in all her reddened glory
she waits, loves for him.

Never will the stains be so bad,
as on that afternoon,
'Glory Street' steps were washed with sea,
Thirty miles inland.

In the parlour, yellow bird sings no more,
It stopped, as did the others, at half-past-four,
For above, down there he listens,
To the tap-tap-tap of the clawing hands,
With ears that cannot hear,
'Mum, When's daddy coming home?'

ROY MITCHELL 16

The Scream

The child screamed, loud enough at first but gradually louder and louder until the sharp, intermittent sounds pierced through my ears like blunt hypodermic needles. Faster and faster they came in the rising hysteria, blotting out the memory of all other sounds, and the ability to think of anything else. My whole body recoiled, but was unable to pull away from the tense elasticity at the source of the sound. My eyes blurred, and the child changed size, now bigger, now smaller. Sometimes he seemed near me, when the pitch of his screaming rose, swallowing me up in the cavernous depths of his mouth. Sometimes, when the noise abated between screams, he seemed to shrink to a tiny dot in the far corner. The child ceased to have an entity and became a noise producing being.

The noise itself was alive. It flew at me, pecking and snapping, violating my senses. It rebounded on the furniture and the walls, it formed layers of sound on chairs and tables so that they hummed and moved with borrowed vibrations.

The sound began to have a destructive effect on the room. It seemed to fly out to distant articles, fix itself there and then try to rebound, bringing the article with it. The child in the centre became the goal for which everything in the room was striving. The room seemed to be caving in, battered and broken up by the reverberations from the screams.

So small a source he seemed, seated on the rug beating his fists on the ground quite ineffectually, since the screaming blotted out all else.

My head felt like a punch ball, and the screams were the extended fists of my young assailant. It was as if he was evoking the powers of nature to bring me, a being who had dared to cross him, down to the ground. In the face of this blinding, deafening, desensitizing opposition I felt totally impotent.

My mind tried vainly to fix itself on some definite idea or action, but the sound swept away the cobwebs of imagination before they had time to form into concrete. My animal instincts began to take over. I could not think, but I could feel, though I had no control over my emotions.

I began to feel vindictiveness against these insults to my sanity, yet I was still powerless to act. Fury took over my brain, I was no longer myself, but an animal grovelling on the floor, trying to beat back the attacking sounds with shouts of my own.

Without realising it, I had grabbed at the child, shaking him as if to remove all last traces of noise from him. He vibrated in my clenched hands and the whole room gave in at last to its dominant temptation and rushed in on me.

I fought, I know, I hit things, I smashed things. I wanted to destroy as the sound had destroyed me, but I was not a thinking human but a powerless animal. The sound had won. It celebrated its victory by robbing me of all my beaten powers.

I welcomed the blackness.

ROSALIND KITCHEN 16

The Inmate

Simplicity reigns. My dad always used to say that. Not that he was simple himself – on the contrary – he was the most complicated man I knew – and yet he looked the same as everybody else. He could burst all the hazy bubbles in his mind, and make everything so simple. Not like me. His mind, I mean. Somehow there's always been something there which made it different for me to look in a mental mirror at myself, than to look at him. Something hidden, yet frustratingly obvious.

My God, I wish they'd let me try. But then, thinking – I suppose they did. And just because I used to knock my building bricks down, and never used the toilet when I was younger, and just because I hit a little girl for calling me a 'big gorm' and she hit her head, and God decided she should be dead at that moment – they put me in here. Not that I'm really blaming God for anything. NO – I've decided He's too good to do people wrong. But I know that it was God that made me just that little bit different from any of 'Them'.

Oh – by the way – my name's Jeffrey. Spelt with a 'J' for Justice, not a 'G' for – well, for God I suppose. Just thought I'd tell you.

89

I call this room my thinking room – all by best thinks happen here. Yes, happen – they don't ever, well, how can I explain? – they don't ever form a big bubble on the way, and then burst their way out so delicately for the world not to hear – they just happen. Come. Come and go.

But this room is just a big waste-bin really – into which I've been screwed up and thrown away – isolated like an infectious and unwanted disease, from a world they say I can't cope with.

See this window here, with the bars on? You know why they've put bars on, don't you? To keep the rest of the world away from me. They envy me, you know, don't they? They're proud to have me, to have found me. They're proud in their wisdom at finding there was something wrong with me, so they put me in here, where they could probe at me safely. But now they've forgotten about me. And so, yet another mind grows cobwebs, shrinks, shrivels, useless to everyone, so they forget about it. Well, I don't care. I've given up caring – it's a bad habit, like smoking – it brings only the negative sort of results, like disease and death.

Ha, death. Death. Everyone spends all of their lives speculating what death will be like, and when it might happen. There's that 'happen' again, you see – they all just come, and then they all go again. Poof! – like that.

And so, then – an invitation. A little nonsensical, perhaps, ruled by the impossibility of it. But, nevertheless, an invitation. To join me in my own experience. Unique experience, may I say. The experience of the Living Dead. A paradox in terms, perhaps, you might say. I'll not argue that, but the aptness of the phrase I'll not easily deny. You see, I am dead. Dead to the world. This room, these four walls, with wallpaper which has fifty-six thousand, three hundred and twenty-eight blood-red roses on, nearly all of which have a name for me to talk with them, this room is my coffin, my tomb. A tomb with a lot of meaning, and tightly closed to stop the parasites of life getting in at me. The walls are hard – the leeches cannot suck the life from that within them, as from the vulnerable blood of more obtrusive beings. Talking of blood, I cut myself yesterday – and somebody came, and somebody put a plaster on for me, and somebody smiled benignly and patted me on the head, and somebody left me alone again. Where was I? Erm – oh yes, Blood – Blood that flows in streams, in rapids of complications, banked in disorder, and carrying the painful recriminations suffered in its warring ways. Life is a constant

90

game for Them – a game of 'Who can shed the most blood, and at the same time lose the least?' Everybody strives to play it safe for themselves, and make life difficult for others – like me.

God – leave me alone, I say – leave me alone. Loneliness is that place where Man can propagate ideas in profusion, and where he is not bothered by the whoring temptations of evil and complexities. He is innocent there, swimming in a crystal clear pool of simplicity.

Yes – you must let me rest for a moment – these words weigh me down so much, even when they have escaped me to linger in the air. And this, my bed, my castle in a sea of uncertainty, a vast ocean where ignorance strikes first, strikes the hardest. From here I rule myself, my world – the world I have had to adapt myself to, in order to live on. They branded me insane with the burning-iron of injustice, and put me in here, in this cage of blackened innocence, with a view to curing my mind of its 'straying hallucinations' and those 'dangerous' complexities of which they are not yet very sure.

Granted, I may be 'simple' as they say, but I know I'm simple only to the extent of being able to see things clearly – to line them up and deal with all my worries one by one, as in a shooting gallery.

You see, I'm not as mad as they would like me to be – that's really why they've put me in here. Here in this 'cooler', if you like, to cool my poor mind to a frosty insanity. Here to eat their plastic foods off their rattling trays which they bring every day from your world to mine, whilst always they wear those white, white coats. 'Leave me alone' I cry to their deaf ears: I lash out at their unfeeling limbs like the caged animal I now am, to free myself from this unworthy womb, and of their obsession with the Darwinian theory; my groping senses endeavour to tear back the bars to be free.

Sobbing, like this now, my tears are groping, groping, searching for their kindness, their estranged kindness, their understanding, their . . . love.

But, sshh – quiet, O silent room – someone is coming. Don't let them know I've been talking – let my words dissolve in the sparkling acid of revelation, and let them dwell in that wondrous realm of simple reality.

STEPHEN DAVID LEDDY 15

Travels in France

Cows graze with strange pedantic decency
Here, where the rock
Is never far beneath the soil,
And the herdsman goes leisurely
To fetch them in the evening.
They walk sonorous down the street
And two children, seated on a haybale
Pattern out an intricate secret game
And barely glance at
The high familiar flanks.
The old woman in black
Tosses the bobbins on her pillow
And counts the hooves
Full and round as cobblestones
And suits her rhythm to theirs.
Sunset, yellow and translucent as a carp
Caught fresh that morning
Fills the sky. The men,
Dustladen, return to the village.
Tomorrow, when the cows set out
The day will be begun.

IMOGEN KATHERINE CLOUT 16

The Unicorn and the Television

The unicorn was young and free,
And wild and white and gold was he.
And galloped, of a summer's day,
Upon the meads a year away.
Adventure-bent, he went to town,
Through the streets walked up and down,
In shop-windows studied prices,
Bought with horn-dust orange-ices.
When behold! inside a box
Struts a clothed and pompous fox.
Unicorn is fascinated:
Coming closer, bumps frustrated
Into glass. At last sees that –

O dire tale! – the fox is flat!
  What monster can it be that flattens
  Foxes into talking patterns?
Unicorn looks behind the screen,
Finds a snake of blue and green,
And two others, brown and black;
Raging, feels he must attack.
Paws the ground and horns the adder –
Nothing happens. Growing madder
Stabs the box, the fox, the lot –
Fox fades into one dim dot.
Hissings smoke out from the monster,
And the manager, who wants to
Call the R.S.P.C.A.
And get this maniac away.

In a zoo in Regent's Park
Lives a unicorn drab and dark.
Fenced-off pens, though bright and light,
Are too confined for his proud might.
And all because he happened to stop
To watch a T.V. in a shop.

KIM TAYLOR 15

Spiral of an ill Wind

The sun slowly fell from the sky, leaving a cold windy night after
it. Suddenly the door of the prison opened, and out stepped Dan,
walking very slowly, head bowed, and with great reluctance. The
yellow light radiated from the interior as a silhouetted officer bid
him good-bye.

'I hope it turns out better for you this time,' he said closing the
door.

'Hugh!' replied Dan scratching his whiskers. Time was near
stillness. All the once busy streets had changed into barren cul-
minating streams of tarmac, taking with it the bright spots of
golden lights radiating down from the street lamps, on its meander-
ing journey through the darkness, disappearing within a few yards
into this darkness one never succeeds to see invade the earth, and
that leaves anguishly at dawn. New York with its growing sky-
scrapers, reaching for the stars, lay hidden behind a net-work of

very brightly lit rectangles and squares, floating parallel to the other. Everything was still silent in this pocket of disguised frenzy. This battle of silence, in the faint whispering wind, was soon shattered as Dan approached the roar and music of a late night snack bar. He quickly rose his bowing head and curiously touched his ears, as if he had never known them to be there, bringing a new phenomena to his freedom.

When he walked in, eyes squinting behind a shielding arm due to the brilliance of the light, he took a seat at the bar and waited to be served, ducking and rubbing his eyes until they got used to the light. The place was empty, then a gang of kids busted in and added more to the dying record.

'Service!' demanded Dan, banging his fist against the counter.

'I'd get outta' here if I were you – nigger boy,' said one of the boys, quite wild looking and rather flushed.

'Why – white boy?'

'Listen here black man,' conceded the boy pointing his finger, 'my friends and me, we don't like to be seen, hanging round the same joint as some lost nigger, so get!'

'Are you mad little white boy?' replied Dan turning around fully. 'You really want a good busting up don't you?' He got off his stool, the kids retaliated forward with an aggressive step, followed by another, until they came almost under Dan's nose. As they stood eyeing each other warily like hawks to his prey of a much greater size, the heat and tensity was soon cooled down when the bar-tender stepped into the scene. Jamas – the kid's name – glanced around.

'About time too,' he said. 'Where've you been?'

'What you want stooge? Beat it!'

The kids hesitantly retired and left.

The cool looking blond leaning against the wall, and holding a duster in the hand against her hip, slowly made forward for Dan, who found his seat and passed his fingers through his wet hair.

'And what can I do for you, lover-boy?' she asked, pushing her face into Dan's.

'Nothing, I was just leaving.'

Some yards from the bar, he was suddenly re-awakened by the loud rolling music.

'Now for pity's sake Dan, let's get outta here, you're free now, we can start all over again. You know them people out there, they don't want to see our faces down them streets. Lets go!' pleaded Dan's mother, crying softly.

'No ma! We ain't gonna move. Can't you get it into your great fat head? We just can't! . . . That's exactly what they want all of us people to do – move and keep on moving, but where to ma? where to ?' he was almost crying. 'White man rule here, he rules there, every corner, every land. We'll soon be thrown out of this planet, but, no! the lord god put us here to live, and live in peace where no white man can throw us out.'

'But . . .'

'No ma! No!' he shouted, wrapping his long fingers around his head, shaking violently about, and sweating, and crying, for an internal pain, beating against his heart. Tightly hugging his round shaped mother he vowed:

'I'll fine a job, ma, any kind of job, anywhere, but I'll sure fine one.'

Tom his younger brother was dumb-founded at the bottom of the stairs, tightly clutching the elaborately incarcerated banister, absorbing all the emotion planted permanently in his brain and grew even stronger as it flourished on the remorse torrents and gales that thickly enveloped his abeyance. The goodness of life was completely lost, while enormous portions of his mind, pregnant with fear, danced inchoately with fire and torment. Suddenly everything became a strange spectrum blurr and he collapsed.

The night grew with chilly breezes. A young boy, maltreated – for wounds and bruises protruded the surface of his face like abnormal muscle growth – appeared on the roof of a casino, by a high brick wall. He would frequently tug at a long rope tied tightly around his waist, with the intent of loosening it, but if anything made it worse. He tried in vain to clamber up the wall, panting and gasping for his breath.

'No pa! I can't do it, I can't!' he cried with the salty tears trickling down his cheeks, forming little streams breaking through the grit and dust that masked his face.

'You just get up that wall, you hear,' retorted his father anguishly, for whispering was not, by far, a great substitute for deep irritating emotional feelings, which he would have carried out, had he not been half way to the summit of a badly constructed casino, in which a window to a good fortune was left unattended to.

The little boy's hands shed blood, and burned, as he traps the tiny sharp bits of dust in his wounds, when he unconsciously clasps his fist. Here from the top, the mechanical music of impatient cars, and the rolling music of the dance halls, the isolated cries of the last newsboy doing late nights, to earn that few more cents, drummed against his body, in the splendour – or rather the abrupt formality of life. Though the air was refreshing it was not to be enjoyed for there was more work ahead.

'Now pass me down the rope,' said his father.

The child stretches out his hand as to receive his father's, but the body of fate blocked that minute space between their trembling fingers, and as that grubby face emerged from behind the wall, his father's stubby fingers seemed more attracted to a loose brick, than his son's. He tipped over and fell howling, and bawling as he spun through the air. Halfway over the edge himself, knelt the boy, stoundered, and beckering with frozen tears on his cheeks, as he watched with marbles eyes, his only friend who caressed and loved him, be devoured into a strange darkness.

With trembling out-stretched arms, Dan exploded out of a nightmare, with streams of sweat washing his face. He gasped for air – he cried and covered his face.

'Oh pa, I'm sorry, god, I'm sorry!' he said.

Dan entered his brother's bedroom.

'Hey kid, you O.K. ?' he said. 'The doctor's gone now,' smiling as Tom opened his eyes. 'Here, what's the idea eh ? Your ma, she thought you were gone then.' Then Dan pinched his cheek and left the room.

Edna – his mother – was just closing the door after the doctor, as Dan appeared at the bottom of the stairs. They both looked at each other with mutual antagonism. His mother stood in a broad fire-red dress, and with tightening eyes looked at Dan, who sighed and peered back.

'Now look,' said Dan, 'don't start this all over again ma.'

'Start what?' she returned, walking away towards the kitchen. Frustrated, Dan hauled his jacket over his shoulders and left.

That evening, the atmosphere of the house was again pervaded with aggression and annoyance, which gave no heed for alliance with Dan and his mother. He ate his tea, nodding from side to side with frustration, knowing that his mother's shifting eyes were piercing him against the bright brown walls of the kitchen. Subsequently, the iron wall that imprisoned within him his tempestual fumes, cracked, and the ice-cold anguish spilled in great tumults.

'O.K.!' he cried. 'So I didn't get that job. That doesn't say we're gonna starve!'

'What about Tom up there?' she nodded.

'You ain't telling me we have not got enough food for all of us.'

'Who's we? Only Tom there, and me, is gonna' eat from them

cupboards. If you had heared me in the first place, we could have been gone from here, and settled down with some friendly face. You could have got a job then – a butler, or a cotten picker, we could have . . .'

'Cotten picker? butler!' shouted Dan. 'What damn thing do you take me for, eh?'

'All I'm saying is, you're gonna fine food for your own guts from now. I ain't gonna' feed you!' Now get out, get!' You god forsaken thing, where you come from, I don't know.' She then put the pot on the table. 'If only your pa was still alive, my,' shaking her head, 'things would have sure worked out better.'

'With money – I went in for two years – that I stole?'

'What money? In my house there is no room for sins. That half woman that still works down at the little bar . . .'

'But that wasn't my child. It wasn't!'

'You get! Get out!'

Just then she rushed over towards a large yellow drawer. It rattled prolongly as she wrenched it open. Immediately, a fork caught her needs. The moment its cold silver met with her stubby finger-tips, she flung it over at Dan, who tried dodging, but his agility was no competition to the high velocity of the assailing fork. It struck him hard on the forehead, then fell to the wooden floor boards, leaving several deep gashes upon Dan's forehead. Quickly reaching for the door, he leapt out like a wild terrified animal, and ripped his jacket as he snatched it off the coat-peg.

His mother was left in an hysteria, stamping on the floor, screaming and flinging the remnants of cutlery from the drawer, all over the kitchen.

A noise-busting car suddenly pulled up at the garage.

'Hey! You, nigger boy,' shouted the driver. 'Stop that car washing and fill her up. Snappy-like! Snappy,' he demanded clicking his fingers. Dan immediately recognized that tinny voice and without hesitation indulged in minding his own business.

'You hear nigger boy? Hey, hey you!' shouted the boy, banging against the car door. 'Nigger boy! Cotten picker! You there!'

'Might you be addressing me?' said Dan, pressing his thumb against his chest, and dropping the hose, and slowly standing upright.

'You see, my ears are kinda' sensative to what people might say, and it's very easy for me to be misled for . . .'

'Listen to this, black man –'

'Hey Dan!' shouted the garage manager suddenly appearing from the shop, 'what's the trouble?'

'Listen to this mister,' said the kid, 'and listen well. Having this here –' he points at Dan, 'cotten picker as one of your decent employees, news could quickly spread around town, and breaking one of our biggest rules, you might just all of a sudden fine yourself, clean out of business, you hear?'

The car departed, without service, then the manager looked at Dan with that doubtful expression. In apprehending these furtive gestures by expressions, which one uses to escape the humiliation in speaking, Dan replied with hazy dissipated hopes for his future. 'Yes, I know.'

The manager, quickly began to rummage through his back pocket and produced a heap of dollar bills from his wallet. 'Here kid,' he said holding them out, 'take this as a kind of compensation.'

'What kind, keep your stinking white money. You made it, so spend it,' and Dan walked away, feeling in his pocket with his fingers, his last cents.

Late that evening, when Dan got home, real stunk-up, his greeting was quite the opposite of what he had anticipated, in fact too much the opposite. He pushed his body against the front door and fell into the house.

'Ma!' he shouted, staggering and swaying perplexed by no harsh reply, nor the quick knock of the pots against the sink, in a dead silence to initiate her presence.

'Ma!' he echoed, bucking from one direction to another. Then suddenly from his fading echoes, came a faint mee-owing of a cat that attracted his docile attention, and lulled him towards the door. It was a young black cat, though outstandingly fat, purring and shining in the badly lit doorway, in the cold air. It lay almost invisible, save for the yellow eyes – flickering in the darkness.

Suddenly the poor creature let out a scream of pain and passion. It struggled fiercely from the captivity of Dan's foot, pressing down hard against its long tail. He bent down and caught it by the scruff of its neck. Seeing the final chance to breathe life again, it clawed and ate at Dan's wrist. But as his wrist shed blood, steaming gently in the wind, his grip tightened around the cat's neck, and he squeezed more and more, ruthlessly. The animal wriggled and heaved, groggling and hissing, as the cloak of death covered it. The air appeared to have become more tense when the poor animal loosened in the creeking summer tide.

MILTON GEORGE PALMER 14

The Game

I

The barest flicker. Nothing more. Just a sudden, hardly noticeable quiver in the smooth flow of his subjective time. But the actual sensation that he felt was irrelevant. After all, if a hundredweight of stone or so falls on you from a height, the actual sensation that you feel as you are flattened to the ground is very brief. But before the sensation you are alive and well. After it, you are quite, quite dead: a totally different state to be in.

Hugh Erikson, before his sensation was alive and well. After it, he was also alive and well. But there all resemblance between the two states ends. For before there were four walls around him and a bed beneath. There was a window ahead of him just dimly visible because of the shallow starlight that shone through. There wasn't much more registering on his darkness-tuned eyes; just vague and shady outlines.

A bed beneath, and four walls round him. And now, a hard and faintly gritty surface beneath and two rising walls on either side. For his bed to have suddenly turned to stone, and two of his walls to have disappeared was bad enough. That at least wouldn't have got such a violent reaction out of him.

That first reaction was a reflex.

'Who the hell turned that damned light on?' No sooner had he said it than he realised what a stupid thing it was to say. The floor of his room was hardly capable of sprouting a tall electric street lamp.

He jumped up and blinked rapidly. Then he began to shake, and the shake progressed into a tremble and his stomach began to feel as if it was falling off a high mountain.

What's happened to me? Where am I? It was only a few seconds before the inevitable stream of thoughts started flowing through his mind, obliterating any attempts at rationalisation that tried to break through the bedlam.

But panic gets one nowhere and, unless a person has no self-control at all, lasts for only a brief period. In Erikson's case it reigned for no more than half a minute. At the end of that time, he began trying to answer the questions his panic had posed. He started off with what his senses told him.

He was in a street, or rather, less than a street–more like an alley. He was standing under the orange light of a street lamp and by that light, he could see that the walls of the alley were a dirty brick, cracked and scratched in many places. Beneath him was a pavement, grey-orange in the light. As far as he could see there were only a few windows in the alley walls, mostly just the dull, dirty brick. Above him, there were a few stars filling the gap between the two black and shadowy walls.

And that was all. The next street lamp was a good two hundred feet away. So Erikson could only see effectively within the extensive pool of light shed by the lamp above him.

Within that, there was no-one. Outside it, his senses told him the situation was the same.

He began to tremble again.

How? Why?

Totally reasonable questions with a series of totally unreasonable answers. Had he somnambulated? Impossible. The time when he had been lying on his bed in his room had been only a few minutes ago. His memory was still sharp and it stated categorically that he had not been asleep. And as he was a human being, he wasn't prepared to start questioning the part of him that formed the basis of his existence.

After a few minutes, he realised that his rationalising powers had met their limit. In situations of less complete unexpectedness, he might have been able to extract some meaning out of his not totally meaningless surroundings and decide on some meaningful course of action. This situation however, was completely unexpected, the surroundings were totally meaningless and as a result he could decide on no meaningful course of action.

He was acting on a reflex when he began to walk up the alley. He was trembling again.

The barest flicker. Nothing more. Just a sudden, hardly noticeable quiver in the smooth flow of his subjective time. But if the transitional sensation was brief and insignificant, the resulting change in what Edward Borley's senses were perceiving was decidedly not so. One moment there was the hard gritty surface of the pavement beneath his feet and the vertical alley walls rising for about 60 feet above him; then the narrow band of stars outshone by the almost lurid orange radiation from the street lamp.

Now those walls had shrunk down to a bare 10 feet above him and two more had appeared. He could feel it. He couldn't see it for all that was visible was a grey blackness broken only by a very faint square of lighter colour. It was not surprising that there was no more information for his eyes, which had previously been bathed in the orange glare of a street lamp, to gather. But he was calm and remained lying on the bed.

The colour-sensitive cones in his retina got less and less effective. His world rapidly dissolved into a faint black and grey. The square of lighter colour resolved into a window, through which shone a few stars. Beneath, there grew a series of dark-against-dark outlines. A chest of drawers?

He got up and felt the first gushes of incredibility.

Why? It wasn't as if something had changed. The fact was that nothing hadn't changed. His whole environment had disappeared and been replaced by surroundings that, in relation to the alley, were totally incomprehensible. It was a physical fact that a bright alley does not turn into a four-walled room within a matter of micro-seconds. So obviously so-called physical facts were nothing more than a jumble of thirteen letters; that is, physical facts derived from previous experience. He was lying on a bed and there were four walls around him. Those were facts, undeniable and completely physical facts. But facts like when-you-let-go-of-a-stone-it-falls-to-the-floor would have to be tested before he could believe in them.

He felt a sense of excitement, but not fear, as he walked towards the chest of drawers and gingerly ran his fingers over its top surface. His sense of touch bore out his sense of sight. That was enough proof for him.

His hands met a small box. He picked it up and, holding it out, let go. Despite the state of mind he was trying to assume, he would have been very surprised to see the box rise slowly to the ceiling. Luckily, what he saw, was in accord with what he wanted to see. The box rattled slightly as it hit the bed. Matches.

He picked up the box again and, withdrawing a match, struck it against one of the rough sides. Its tip broke into a sudden balloon of light which quickly subsided into a faint and flickery yellow.

Perfectly normal, he thought.

The matches were normal, the gravity was normal, the chest of drawers was normal, the stars were normal. The only thing that was completely abnormal was his presence.

He found a light switch and pulled it down. The room was alight with white-yellow light. He pushed it up. Darkness. On-light. Off-darkness.

He rapped his knuckles against the wall. Sound. Completely unmistakeable sound. He opened his mouth and gurgled. Again his brain told him, sound. He whispered. He hit himself. Sound. Pain.

There was no doubt left in his mind. He was here and here was here. He existed and the objects that he saw existed. This was no flickering, uncontrollable dream. He was master of himself and, to a certain extent, of his environment. If he could drop a box of matches and turn on a light, then he could overturn a chest of drawers and drill a hole through the wall.

But whatever he did, there was no point in lingering here, to damage the furniture, mess up the walls or anything. He would have to see what was around him.

He opened the door and looked out onto a dark passageway. Opposite him was another door with a just visible number, 87.

An apartment building, he suggested to himself. To his left he could see a narrow carpet, running down the centre of the passageway. At the latter's end was another window but even less distinct than the one in the room he had just left. Immediately beside him was a rectangular table pushed against the wall. But there was no colour. Everything was grey and black.

Ordinary night vision he thought. In fact if there was anything at all wrong with the scene, he must have been acting incredibly obtusely not to have noticed it.

He walked across the passageway and noticed that the crack under the door was no lighter than the door itself. He decided that just entering, not certain whether the place was being lived in or not, was rash. He didn't relish the idea of meeting anyone until he had explored a bit more thoroughly; at least not in that fashion, as if he was some furtive burglar.

Acting on this decision, he rang the bell and retreated under the table on the other side of the passage. After at least three minutes no-one had opened the door. He acted accordingly.

Inside, he found a light switch and flicked it down. No-one.

The room must have been some sort of a drawing-room. There were two arm chairs, a book-case, a side-lamp, etc. The room was much the same in size and shape as the previous one; it had just been furnished in a different way. The other rooms included a kitchen, a bathroom and a bedroom. Nothing was unusual; the bath had two taps, one of which gave hot water, the other, cold. There were radiators, towels, soap, sinks, chairs, beds; not one unrecogniseable object. After ten minutes, he slipped out.

He repeated the bell-ringing procedure with the next door. Within a minute, he heard the sound of slow dragging footsteps and the crack beneath the door turned yellow-white. And then the door opened.

He, crouched beneath the table, became suddenly excited and suddenly relieved. A man with two legs and two arms was standing in the door-way, bleary-eyed, blinking and dressing-gowned.

'Who's there?' Same language. Same voice-pattern. Same accent. Same inevitable irritation. The man looked to either side of him, shrugged and closed the door again.

The excitement and relief quickly subsided. With an environment so exactly similar in every detail, what else could have appeared in that doorway. A butterfly? A rattlesnake? He was undoubtedly on his own world.

He explored two more uninhabited apartments. That is, two out of the five that he tried.

When he came to the sixth, he was just about prepared to meet some-one. But just as he had his thumb over the bell-push and was about to press it down, he heard a sound which made him drop his hand and listen.

Someone was crying.

II

In the beginning, there was Something and a disc of probabilities, infinite in extent. In the beginning, therefore, when it was flat, there was strictly-speaking nothing – just an infinite collection of might-have-beens and could-have-beens.

Something and nothing.

But Something decided to start doing things with this disc. After all, it was there and as there was no-one else, he might as well make use of it. And so he set out on something which was to consume his entire life. Which was infinite.

He folded the disc along one of its chords and turned the segment over until it met some of the rest of the disc.

Before we see what happened where they met, an analogy might be appropriate. A coin lying on a table is, in a way, a probability. It has the potentiality of being thrown and landing with either heads or tails facing upwards. And a human with a useable arm standing by that coin, is another probability because he has the potentiality of picking up the coin and tossing it. So the coin is the maybe-heads and maybe-tails and the man is maybe-I-toss-it. When the man does toss it, the two potentialities are realised, the two 'maybes' or rather the two probabilities meet, and probability turns into reality.

So Something folded the disc along a chord. Some of the probabilities touched.

The first moment of reality was born.

Something viewed what he had created. It was a huge sea of gas and dust. Something folded another part of the disc and new probabilities met. He viewed the reality again and found that in certain places the gas and dust, because of its uneveness, was in the process of forming into lots of little pockets, contracting under their own gravity. Something could see the trend. He began to fold more rapidly, bringing more and more probabilities into play. The pockets contracted into galaxies and some of the galaxies drew towards each other and formed clusters. Inside the galaxies, stars formed and around the stars, planets condensed and began to orbit these stars.

In many ways, Something was like a computer. He could let the automatic side of him take over, automatically seeing the trends that the interplay of probabilities was producing and automatically acting upon them. It was the equivalent of a sub-conscious. So when the task of folding the disc got boring, he would let this sub-conscious take over. (For although at the beginning he had been able to make fairly large jumps, from a sea of gas and dust to the beginning of galaxies, now when things were much more complex, he had to be much more careful and the progressive changes had to be millimetric.)

And then life appeared.

It was time for Something to consciously intervene. Up to now, his automatic side had been doing most of the work and there hadn't been much to interest him. Now the fruit of his intelligence and patience had been rewarded. Now he could start enjoying himself.

While letting his sub-conscious get on with the other life-forms, Something concentrated on one particular species, because it showed signs of getting on the fastest. It inhabited the third planet of a very average star on the edge of a very average galaxy. Through Something's careful handling, it went from complex organic molecules in a sea which originally covered practically all its world's surface area, to fish, to reptiles, to mammals – through apes to an upright white or black-skinned biped.

And intelligence.

Here was something really worth his while. Because of his infinite selection of probabilities, he could amuse himself in any way he wanted. He played jokes with individual bipeds. For instance, he allowed certain members of the species to develop certain unusual powers which the others did not possess and were therefore afraid of. This resulted in the uncommon specimens getting burnt alive. Very funny. But he was getting bored of that one so he let the creatures' fear of abnormality grow less.

He played jokes with whole groups of bipeds. For instance making one group provoke the other into bouts of mass-murder. Funny, but getting rather stale as it kept on happening.

Soon he reckoned he had played out most jokes involving the interaction of different bipeds. Now was time for something new. The other life species weren't intelligent enough yet to have much of an effect.

It was not long before he had thought of an idea. He could make the bipeds interact with another probability of themselves. The latter operation was fairly easy to achieve.

He searched back into his perfect memory for the probability interactions that had produced the life-form. Then he looked around in his selection until he found virtually identical probabilities, only different in that this new probability would develop on a different but very similar planet. Then, while he left his subconscious to monitor the bipeds making sure that they didn't change very much, he began to bring the probabilities into play and the new life form began. As he had virtually done it all before, he could accelerate the process. Organic molecules-fish-reptiles-mammals-apes. Any change that the process induced on the other bipeds, his sub-conscious was careful to cancel with more probabilities. In a very little time, the new bipeds were ready for Something's adjustment to their thinking – a very fundamental adjustment. It was the basis of the joke.

As he continued he was careful to keep the life-form just like the other bipeds so as to give the joke maximum effect.

Finally they were ready for the joke itself, with of course no knowledge that they had been hustled up for the purpose. Then Something froze everything while he paused to consider the correct probabilities which would induce the correct circumstances. (The life-forms were of course not aware of this pause.) He would swap two of the bipeds, each from their respective worlds into the other's.

So when Something started work again, all the bipeds were unaware that anything unusual had happened.

All, that is, except for two.

III

He strained his ears through the wooden barrier of the door. The crying was soft and jerky and sounded as if it had been continuing for some time. There were the outward gasps of breath, hiccoughing out in quick succession, then the gurgling and hastily indrawn sniff.

The crying stuttered to a stop. Silence for a moment and then faint muttering. 'I dnt wanna liv an'more.' He could hardly make the words out. But the muttering became slightly clearer.

'I wanna dy.' The crying broke out again, louder and more violent.

'Dy. Dy. I want to Dy.' The words, hysterical, almost screamed, came through the door in almost perfect clarity. And he suddenly realised what it was talking about.

'I want to die.' He felt his mind reel. He became almost unaware of his new environment. Someone in there was having the Difficulty. He had never seen, heard, touched or in any way come into contact with the Difficulty, but he knew it to exist. Like most people, it gave him a morbid excitement when he thought of it, but to actually hear it in operation just on the other side of a door made his head feel as if it was one mass of roaring blood. This excitement was, like most emotions, irrational. It probably came about because of the thought that he could be of use and help the person suffering the agony of the Difficulty; it was, after all, the most important fundamental in anyone's life. But before the thought had always been a fantasy; now it was a very real possibility, if not a certainty.

The crying grew louder. 'Someone kill me,' came the hysterical sobs. And then, as if giving reason to itself: 'I want to die.'

He made up his mind. He stealthily slipped open the door and padded towards the figure, faintly silhouetted against a window. The window was open and the person was crouching on a chest of drawers, level with its sill.

He was nearly there when the floor creaked and the figure suddenly turned round. It was a she.

'Who are you?' she cried.

'It's all right.' And before her mind could gather what was happening, he had reached out with lightening speed and given her a strong push. Her not very stable balance broke and she toppled out of the window.

The tremble in Hugh Erikson's stomach was getting louder and more violent. His eyes, hardly visible in the faint orange glow from the next street lamps, with their pupils greatly expanded gave the impression of being yawning black holes reaching down into his brain. His hands quivered by his sides and he walked as if on slippery butter.

He was frightened and his body felt and showed it. What was more frightening was that he couldn't control his terror. And what was more frightening still was that he didn't know how he'd got here or where he was. Now, he could hardly be sure who he was. Which wasn't just frightening: it made him feel as if he was walking around inside a nightmare.

He was beginning to feel himself constrict all over when he came into the light of the lamp. Even if it was a lurid nightmarish orange it was still light. And light illuminated things and banished shadows which his feverish mind turned into any frightening shape it could think up. Ghosts and ghouls and spirits didn't exist so well in light, or, if they did were not so intangible.

Erikson's mind calmed a bit, his body grew more controllable and the constriction stopped.

Between him and the next lamp was a hundred foot gulf of darkness. But it was all he could do.

After about fifty feet, his mind and body started again with their uncontrollable outflows of fear. The fear had seemed slightly remote under the lamplight but with increasing distance had got increasingly less so.

But after a few more strides, he first became aware that he was hearing voices. His initial reaction was fear; a sudden surge of intense almost palpable fear. But that died almost as soon as it had arisen.

They weren't whispered voices. They were speaking voices, faint only because of distance. They weren't elusive voices, disappearing as soon as you concentrated on them. They remained fixed.

Ghosts don't talk. People talk.

Erikson began to run and the voices grew clearer and louder. They were definitely people. Ghosts don't obey the laws of acoustics.

He stopped out of breath at a black gap in the wall. On closer inspection, it turned out to be another very narrow alley, no more than two pavements wide. He looked into it and just saw another wall at the other end. It was clearly a narrow connecting alley between two streets.

107

But Erikson was sure that the sound was coming from that other street. Calming himself, he began to walk along the alley. The voices got nearer. Then they stopped. Erikson hurried on and came onto the street.

For a moment his fear almost vanished at the sight of ordinary human beings. But then it thrust back like a plunging dagger.

There were two men standing under a street lamp. One held a gun to his temple, his face almost devoid of expression. He pulled the trigger. Then there was blood and torn skin shrouding his face in a ludicrously unreal mask, while the area round his temple was smashed inwards.

Erikson screamed and the other man whirled round. Erikson could hear nothing for the blood in his head and all he could see were blotches of violent red against blackness. He fainted. As he fell, the back of his head caught the sharp corner of the wall and he broke his neck.

IV

'The court is in session.' The judge banged the gavel and the murmuring died down.

Borley was in a dream, he was sure of it. He was standing in a wooden stand, his hands leaning against the wooden bannister. The wood was solid, it was touchable, it was completely hard. In was completely un-dream-like. So was the surface he was standing on. So were the people he was looking at. So was everything. Which made the fact that it must be a dream even more incomprehensible.

Could it not be? As he asked himself the question he remembered that night. The sudden scream that had ensued after the girl had gone out of the window had baffled him for a moment before he remembered that she had had the Difficulty. But even so, should her mind have protested so violently to Termination?

And then there were the sirens and the flashing lights and the police and the cell. He would have terminated himself if it hadn't been for his intense curiosity.

They had made him sign statements saying that he had killed her. Perhaps they thought it might have hurt her.

'It can't have hurt,' he had told them. 'It was too quick.' They had just looked blankly at him. Then one of them had angrily retorted: 'Is that all you've got to say, you dirty murderer.'

Now he was being tried. For what? 'Murder' they called it. But what the hell that meant, he had no idea. The charge had read:

Edward Borley is charged with murder of the first degree. Why? What?

The session went on. Witnesses were called. Prosecution asked questions. Defence asked questions. The latter had a note of hopelessness in his voice.

It's like trying to find excuses for a moron, he thought. That fool in the stand admits that he's done it but effectively says 'so what?' What can I do with a cretin like that? The feeling of all the people in that court room whole-heartedly against him could almost be felt.

But Edward Borley saw it all as if it was a play being acted out in front of him. He was desperately thinking, trying to find an explanation for everything. But his mind refused to function. It was out of control unable to follow any logical train of thought.

Pull yourself together. The command to himself somehow worked. His mind calmed and he was once more able to control himself. He started rationalising.

These people were protesting violently against him helping someone who was suffering from the Difficulty. His people did no such thing. Therefore, his people were different from these people. The latter regarded killing as criminal.

It suddenly dawned on him. His mind stood numb as he let the thought filter through it. His eyes opened wide and his mouth fell open in complete astonishment. They didn't know. They hadn't found out.

But how could it be? A people so superficially similar, yet so fundamentally different. But it was the only explanation. His mind could not fathom the concept, but objectively, he knew it must be so.

He would wait for a chance to speak.

He could hardly force himself to do this as the trial dragged on. At last, the judge turned to him.

'Have you anything to say in your defence?' he said.

Now he would tell them.

'Yes,' he replied, 'and I ask you not to interrupt me while I am doing so.' He braced himself. He would have to choose his words carefully.

'Before now, I have been completely baffled as to why it has been thought so terrible for me to have killed someone or as you put it, to have committed murder.' There was a rising murmur from the court. Borley raised his voice. 'I now understand.' The murmur lowered. 'But before you can appreciate my previous bafflement you must understand the society in which I lived.

'Far back in our history – I don't know when – it was discovered that to die is really rather insignificant. It was not exactly a discovery but a theory so convincing that no one has questioned it since. It was realised that we are all the same person. We are all one infinite life. But the anomaly is that we began to exist with an ingrained incomprehension of infinity. We cannot understand it so we fear it. Because of this, we divide our infinite life into finite sections. And these finite sections are our so-called "lives". When we are born into these lives, we obviously cannot remember the previous ones because that would mean we would be aware of our whole infinite life stretch.

'The people I see around me are reflections of my other lives. But to someone else I would be a reflection of one of his other lives. So it is all relative. This is because all the lives live at once. It would be stupid, as this is the case, to expect that a person living his life would be alone. He would see some of his other lives but would not identify himself with them, thus he does not meet with the concept of infinity. As each new person is born, we come into contact with more and more of this infinite life, although we are not aware of it as such.

'Everything exists at once, but we seem to be going from past to future because our "now" moves through the eternal present of our lives and gives the impression of time progression. The situation is actually more complex, but this is enough to get the idea.

'So in our society, when someone doesn't want to live anymore, he kills himself. But there are some people who for some reason have an aversion to this and cannot terminate their lives. This is called the Difficulty. When I went into that girl's room I found her crying and saying she wanted to die. I had every reason to believe she had the Difficulty and so I killed her. That a fuss should be made over that seems to me totally ludicrous . . .'

There was rising bedlam. Then someone from the jury called, 'Never heard so much bull in my life.'

'Quiet,' retorted the judge and banged the gavel. He paused and then began speaking. 'This is a criminal proceedings which passes judgements based on English law. The statement you have just made, in the law's eyes is complete nonsense and therefore will not be taken into consideration. I therefore pronounce you guilty of murder of the first degree and sentence you to life imprisonment. The court is adjourned.'

In the rising volume of voices that ensued, Borley got up onto the bannister and, tensing his muscles, jumped off backwards. Termination was all that was left.

He would be bound to break his neck.

V

Something stopped work and felt very amused. It was a good start. Both bipeds dead. But what other jokes could be play?

JONATHAN GEORGE COX   15

Boldly I opened the door and went in

Boldly I opened the door and went in.

Newton's cradles rock gently to and fro, suspended in the air by a cavalry of sea-horses with tails interlocked. A maroon daffodil floats towards me, swimming casually, its fins in the shape of leaves, flapping harmlessly against its thighs. It gawped at me amiably from two blemishes on its lower gills, curiously resembling petals, whilst its mouth rhythmically opened and shut in a useless manner.

Below, a patch of grave-stone crosses were springing up out of the wax, white, strange and strained with the efforts of growth. The crosses were flexible and their inscriptions not yet fully developed: blurred and immature.

A sound infiltrated into my drugged senses, distant, yet all around me. Dogs with tin-can faces raced in the wax, and sung bubbles at me. I smelt onions: sweet, unmistakable onions, pungent, odorous onions, enticing, luring onions, erotic, seductive onions. They seemed to be coming from the moon. I reached out and caught a passing star, which gave me a ride there. When I got to the moon it was Autumn, and the elves were falling from the trees, and littering the parks. In one of the park-bench legs was a door. I straightened myself out and

Boldly I opened the door and went in.

Onions, onions, a haven of onions. Onions . . . riding bareback on cushions stuffed with plucked chickens. Onions . . . sliding down the edge of razorblades and laughing, while the transparent secretion of the razors' blood oozed into the river of raspberries. Onions . . . reciting Cuneiform backwards in four-time, and teaching priests their catechisms. Onions . . . playing ball with big round women with my mother's face, bouncing them, and watching them turn blue and purple. Onions . . . wearing dog's tin-can faces: Cola, 'eaches, 'einz, pineapl', Coca.

Suddenly an ugh appears, writhing on its belly, devouring any unfortunate onions available. It stinks of fresh soap and bath salts, and squirms its way along, leaving a trail of disembowelled onions stark, raw and gnawed. A piano stealthily lurching behind some polka-dot bushes, apparently yawns and barrs its half-decayed teeth, and, with the snap-dragon motion of an alligator, it snaps its jaws to with the ugh safely mangled inside. I watch with mild interest. I scream. Nothing happens, so I scream again, waiting for something to happen: a door appears.

Boldly I opened the door and went in.

A deserted battlefield. Grenadiers throw flowers over each other. Somebody fires a shot, which half-heartedly limps out of the barrel, unsteadily totters, falters, and falls down dead into the rich, deep-pile carpet. I walked past them and down the street, which was blocked half-way down by a transparent wall. Through it, rain trickled off the trees made of crystalised orange peel, and flowers fell from heaven. The pigs and goblins put up their ornamental umbrellas to keep dry from the petals, and the caterpillars crept into their crêpe cottages. A brick in the wall was loose.

Boldly swinging the brick back I slid through.

A brass rubbing got up and walked away. The statues whispered peevishly amongst themselves and turned away at the pregnant Venus de Milo with the hare-lip. A brass bed, ninety hands high was down below me, in a pit. The pillow was transvessing images, changing and blurring. A grotesque image assembled itself and faded silently into oblivion. The screen altered, and a young girl was there, hurt by a graze, and being suffocated by well-meaning affection. Glimpses of her childhood flitted past, reappearing ghosts, just for an instant. The train carried them off, and I longed to recapture these lives. I jumped down the pit, to meet the train – but I kept falling and falling. A lift passed me, on its way up, '. . . neteenth floor, ladies' crocodile eyes for extra-special occasions in a variety of beautiful hues to fit all sizes, men's clothes, and our car salesrooms with the latest four-speed caterpill . . .'

I met a hand, looking rather lost, so I caught it and attached it to my right thigh, for convenience: it looked much happier. Still flying through the air I noticed a number of other people, apparently also flying in the air, with various additional limbs affixed

112

to their bodies in diverse fashions. This must be their chosen vocation, I decided, and passed an angel with white whiskers, muttering that he was late.

Landing in a bank of clouds, I observed that my size was decreasing again, but not that of my assumed hand. Awkwardly, I hauled my hand after me, whilst crawling backwards, and came upon a town infested and polluted with life. The windows were made with bricks and there was a living chess set by the side of a molten chocolate lake. It appeared a normal day and life seemed to be continuing as usual: a quaver skipped merrily by and a sting-ray, with a triangular head, large, bloated body, several tentacles and four sets of wings (striped) pranced by, singing traditional Egyptian obscenities. A shutter was flapping enticingly, so

Boldly I unveiled the window and went in through the bricks.

Darkness. Cold. Stench. Death. A single beam of light revealed to my acute horror and fear, sawing off one of its beards with a comb, the most lurid . . .

The struggling young writer stopped scribbling and examined his manuscript. He scrapped it after reading it, and started again in a different style.

Boldly I opened the door and went in.

I was in a room. It was light and airy. It was big. I felt small. There were two other men. They were by a piano. Mantovani seemed to be striking something up with Liberace. It seemed promising I went to –

HELEN EDITH SHENTON 14

I see paper people

I see paper people with bullets through their eyes
with axes in their thighs.
I see walking pigs with 'Danish' on their backs
wearing fluorescent rain-proof macs.
I see stunted orange chickens with skinhead braces
with King Lion imprinted faces.
I see plastic supermarkets advertising an increase in prices
such petty vices.
I see grey rainbows and multi-coloured skies
strung with fish that fly.
I see one-storey flats and high-rise bottle kilns
where you can see pretty blue films.
I see a labyrinth of drainpipes in mulberry and blood

protruding out of sanguine mud.
I see harassed daughters with toes asking why
while mother's getting high.
I see ten-legged octopuses making gentle pornography together
in yellow fields of heather.
I see militant workers striking for less pay
because the machines won't lay.
I see piano-playing teeth with voices like larks
and goblin-eating harps.
I see lights which tell the time and clocks to read by
for when you die.
I see death as being desirable and my own escapism
being sentenced to this prism.
I see the twisted world from this straightforward cell
my own private hell.
I see a distorted view of your outside life
as straight as a mangled knife.

HELEN EDITH SHENTON 14

Scorpion

I – *The Capture*

The slight rustle in the shrubs brought a small boy running, his large black eyes widened with excitement. Another rustle; and slowly the boy crept up to the active shrub and gave it a sharp 'whack' with his stick. As a small creature scuttled frantically away, the urchin dropped his hessian bag on his prey, and with a victor's whoop of delight scooped it up and tied the neck. Holding the bag to the sun, he watched in fascination as it jumped, and stretched and convulsively shook. For that moment he was far in spirit from the dull surroundings of the Greek plain, until his study was interrupted as a wooden cart badly in need of oiling rumbled over the hot sand. For a few moments the boy's expression grew fierce and troubled, but then vanished as he turned to run to the cart, kicking little dust clouds where previously his feet had been. In the driver's seat sat an upright old man, his dry, wrinkled, sand-stained skin, evidence of the sun's maltreatment. He was no more than fifty, yet he resembled a man who had had the experience of life for seventy years. His one and only companion stood on the sand at the receiving end of the reins he was holding; as worn out with life's monotony as his master. The cart jerked as the small boy clambered on, acting as a cue for the donkey to go. The journey was as it was always was, silent and unfriendly: the boy being engrossed in the activities of his hessian bag and the old man gazing watery-eyed ahead of the landscape of brown baked plain.

The horizon broke at last to reveal a tiny village, one church and 16 houses being its only contents. The decrepit old man gave a sharp tug on the reins, and with the understanding that only comes out of fifteen years companionship and respect, the donkey stopped. The jolt once more brought the passenger reeling back to his senses, and thrusting the bag deep down into his vest he remembered to wave his thanks to the tired old-timer. Turning now, the boy leaped over a straw fence pausing once only to greet some village widows in his usual half-hearted manner, he gambolled into the yard, dutifully shutting the gate as he did so. At the top of the yard was a small stone house, which made no attempt whatsoever to conceal its total state of neglect and dilapidation. The paint-stripped door was wide open, and as he approached the boy recognised his mother's voice; the other was a man's.

II – *The Collection*

His mother turned round sharply and, seeing her son, told the man to leave.

Now wiping her hands on her apron and adopting a care-free smile, she addressed her son,

'How was school today Costa?'

Costa blinked, he had quite forgotten about school, but nevertheless he dared not tell his mother the truth. The truth? She wouldn't believe it anyway. How could he explain to her that he spent a whole day just thinking, when she could not endure Church meditation for over an hour?

'Alright Mama,' he replied uneasily, and then quickly noticing her disappointed expression; 'Padre said I was making excellent progress!'

The enormity of the lie seemed worth the radiant smile it brought to his mother's lips.

Taking his hand impulsively, she led him to the gallipot (a small glazed, earthen-ware pot) which was on the table, and sheepishly produced from it a small bar of chocolate.

'Look Costa,' she watched his eyes in anticipation of his reaction, 'for you.'

Costa managed a forced smile at his mother: she made him feel so ashamed, so unworthy . . . almost.

'Thank you Mama.'

He reached out for the chocolate but withdrew it instinctively as he felt a small scratch near his thigh. He grinned inwardly as he thought, 'my conscience in a hessian bag!'

Noticing his mother's concern he quickly added, 'But first I must read.'

He walked to the back of the large room, and cautiously threw a glance over his shoulder at his mother who was however otherwise occupied. This corner of the room was his, and even though it only consisted of a bed, suitcase, and wooden box, it was the only place where he could feel absolute privacy. Carefully he removed the hessian bag from his vest and put it on his bed. He bent under his bed and produced a large, rough, wooden box (formerly a tomato crate) which also was placed on the bed. His tongue lolling over his mouth, he delicately undid the lock with the ease, skill and experience of a professional 'safe-breaker'. The visible result could quite easily have proved fatal to one of nervous disposition. Inside was an array of small 'cells' partitioned off by scraps of cardboard. In each cell was a hideous scorpion, each varying in size and horror, each one worse than the last. These horrifying creatures were all alive, and at the arrival of light a general shuffle began. Costa smiled, with a true collector's satisfaction, now at last he had got the biggest scorpion he knew of, and consequently his collection was now complete. As he undid the neck of the bag and dropped the tiny nightmare into the last remaining box, his eyes seemed to take on an apathetic glaze, that only a disturbed man could assume. He was awoken from his stupor as he heard his mother call for him, and hastily he packed away his precious collection, and when ready, went hungrily to lunch, with the appetite of one well-pleased with the day's fortunes.

III – *Reconciliation*

Dawn broke early the next day, or so it seemed to Costa. After quickly washing and dressing he ran back into the desert land. All yesterday's surroundings seemed non-existent, and the plain seemed fresh and new. It had always been so with Costa, he could perceive in Nature what others could not, he could sense the rejuvenation of each new day, he could smell her sweet goodness and innocence; it was to Costa as if Nature was an everforgiving mother who gave her children a new healthy place to live in every day, so that they might learn to love it and use it properly, not abuse and swathe it in rubbish and sin. How bitterly Costa felt when neighbouring lechers held their feasts on 'his' land, and how keenly he shared his mother's (Nature's) wrath; when she would rant, roar and weep, Costa saw this as thunder, lightening and the ensuing rainfall. Everything was clear to Costa, because he sincerely believed that he was chosen by Nature to become her messenger, her predestine. That is why each morning he would arise early and watch dawn break, and in the serenity of the sleepy village, Costa could imagine what glorious fate lay in store for him. Only when the first bird crossed the sky would Costa run back to the house, and undress and feign sleepiness until his mother awoke.

This morning, Costa was still full of the glory of the previous night's conquest, and he lay in bed watching the sleeping form of his mother rise and fall as she breathed.

Today was Sunday, and subsequently no school! After church he would go down to the brooklet in the valley, and for the rest of the day he would go and tease Thomas's donkey, maybe even Thomas!

What simple happiness could be achieved first by thinking and imagining. Why no one else understood, Costa didn't know, but he put it down to his fate. Now he heard his mother get up, and when she had completely shaken off her mantle of sleep she began dressing herself. Peeping through the coarse bed sacking Costa could see his mother now; how beautiful she was, he thought, how nobly she held her head, and how carefully she dressed herself. Costa knew that she didn't belong here, in this hovel: she was of a fine cast. But she had been left with a fatherless child, through her innocence and absolute trust in mankind. Her parents hadn't understood and had thrown her out. From that day onwards it had been downhill, gleaning, begging, the degradations grew with time. Costa wondered what she worked as now: it often used to puzzle him, and why did he find a different man with his mother when he came home . . .?

Despite her simplicity and lack of understanding he loved her passionately, and one day he would take her away from all this and give her everything that she so richly deserved.

This pensive mood was, however, shortlived as his mother was now calling him for breakfast.

The meal over, Costa's mother put on her shawl and head-scarf and wrapping her bible in her white pocket handkerchief said consequentially;

'I'll go to the church alone this week as I have something I must talk to the padre about, do you understand?'

Costa understood. He knew his mother got depressed, and that she liked to talk the padre, to soothe her feelings of guilt. She had done this before.

Being left alone, Costa could think of nothing but his scorpions, and so he cleared away the dirty mats that they ate from, and took his mother's washing outside to dry in the yard.

The thrill and immense enjoyment it gave Costa to examine his collection was abnormal. It was almost an infatuation for imprison-ing and torturing live things that Costa had. He moved slowly to his beloved converted tomato crate and bending down he undid the lock. There they were, hungry and active, jauntily scuttling from side to side, climbing and nearly reaching the top only to fall back again.

Sometimes, Costa revelled in the idea of removing the cardboard partitions, and watching them fight one another: at first advancing and retreating, then the braver, tearing the appendages off their opponents, rendering them senseless, so as to uncurl the fatal tail!

Costa gazed in pride at each in turn, but was startled when he noticed that his prize and most recent speciment was inactive, just lying motionless on the floor of the box. With a trembling lip and wavering heart he gave a sudden rap to the box. The scorpion leapt and as if just having woken, it pranced around the cell. Costa was greatly relieved: but time gave little opportunity for this, because Costa's mother was entering the yard.

'Costa!' she shouted, her anger evident: 'Why have you put my washing outside?'

Costa was always wary and he had a good reply ready.

'Because I thought it would dry better in the sun, Mama.'

Her voice softened as she lightly reminded him;

'You know that anything left outside gets stolen, and they are my best linens.'

Costa chuckled wryly, 'they were her only linens!'

His mother came in folding her shawl, and when she had put it away she drew up a chair for herself and beckoned Costa to her. Costa sensed her misery but somehow he couldn't comfort her, but nevertheless he did as she said. She grasped his hands and looked at him firmly in his eyes. Painfully she began:

'Costa do you enjoy school?'

Costa had dreaded that the padre had told his mother the truth and now his fears were confirmed. But he truthfully replied;

'No Mama.'

'Oh, Costa if the boys are bullying you there, I'll . . .' her voice sounded alien and hostile.

Costa cut in; 'No Mama it's not that.'

Costa watched his mother pitifully trying to think of another reason, but despairingly she shook her head and then harshly enquired:

'Why then, Costa?'

Costa heaved, for the first time in his life he was going to try to make her see, to understand, to share his great idea. His fists drummed relentlessly on the table as he tried to give his words the full impact of their meaning.

'Mama, school teaches you facts, figures and manners, but it doesn't teach you to appreciate. It tells you to be satisfied with what you have, and look no further. It tells you to believe without finding out for yourself.'

The words tumbled from his lips in an unsteady stream.

'Mama, do you know how I feel, when I'm alone on the plain? I feel rich, and well-fed; I feel hopeful, I think then that I may escape from all this,' he indicated the hovel, 'that I might be someone. I feel that this is a box, and that there is light outside, which is why I must escape, and follow the light. Mama, please say you understand.'

Costa breathed a long contented sigh of relief, he had got it all off his chest at last. He watched her face as it twisted in pain and anguish. Poor Mama. She didn't understand, she might lie and say she did, but deep down Costa knew that she never could.

Finally she pursed her lips and admitted, 'Costa, I don't, I can't but if you have hope you will achieve; I do believe that.'

A long awkward silence intervened until Costa crestfallen, left the house.

IV – *Affrontal*

For a few moments Costa was unsure of what to do: a dry lump still choked him, but as Costa walked and saw, his spirits rose. He had walked in the direction of a neighbouring village, Skathos, which Costa excitedly recalled was a tourist attraction. Although Costa opposed violation of the laws of nature, he was not averse to progress. As it was Sunday (market-day) there were many tourists in the village and Costa's heart leapt as he saw a shiny automobile in the stables. Only twice in his life had Costa seen an automobile before: to him it was the most desirable thing one could possibly possess. He could almost imagine himself behind that shiny plastic steering wheel. How proud his mother would be!

Costa's immense and total admiration for the automobile, prevented him from hearing the jostling, jeering, laughing crowd that approached him.

'Do you like the car, Sonny?' asked one red-nosed hunk of a tourist.

'Yes!' Costa felt good to be seen talking to tourists, and so he emphasized his answer.

The tourist's friends all laughed wildly, which Costa mistook for friendliness.

'Do you know much about cars?' the tourist asked after quietening his friends.

Costa's chest swelled with pride: he didn't actually, but he wasn't going to say so, 'Yes I know a good deal about them.'

The tourists exploded with uncontrollable mirth and Costa felt that at least he could talk to them and they'd understand. So he did. He told them everything; about his collection, his feelings, his mother, and his destiny. There was only a suppressed giggle for reply.

At last the tourist said,

'O.K. Sonny I'd like to take a picture of you.'

Costa was apprehensive, 'Me?'

'Yes, that's right,' the tourist retorted, 'I want a last snap-shot of a typical, Greek, village boy.'

Costa felt strung, rebuked, hadn't he explained? He wasn't the typical, Greek, village boy, he was Special. The whole crowd started to laugh wildly, loudly, inanely, happy because they'd had their fun.

Costa, turned crest-fallen, his ears bursting with their cruel laughter: then broke into a wild arm-flinging run.

It was darker now but Costa could still make his way across the plain, after all wasn't he a 'typical village boy'. He had thought they understood. The sheer depression of rejection upset the economy of his mind. For Costa, it was a lonely walk back to the house.

V – *Death and Life*

Costa arrived at the house by nightfall, hot, dusty, and tear-stained. His mother was already asleep; he was glad, he didn't want her to see him like this. Costa flopped onto his bed, exhausted from his emotional reasoning. As he lay, confused and frightened, he heard a small shuffle coming from under his bed. His scorpions! With fumbling hands he put the box on his bed and fumbled until the lock was open. With a horrible dread of the result he slowly, slowly lifted the lid. There were all his scorpions, all dormant and listless except for his prize one. This terrifying desert insect was frantically scrambling to escape. Costa knew it was impossible but he did not foresee the coming event. The scorpion turned on its hard armoured back revealing a tender pink spot on its underside, menacingly the venom-charged tail drove into this, again and again until all that remained was a bristle, black corpse, completely void of life.

Costa sat staring for a few moments at the armoured wreck and then showing no emotions of grief, he picked up the box, tip-toed past his mother's bed, out into the yard, then further to the plain where, with complete control, he tipped the box upside down into the sand and watched his prisoners escape one by one and scuttle off into oblivion.

Slowly he walked, a pathetic figure, back to the house. The time for crying was over, he knew that, the time for regret was over, he knew that too. But like bad dreams they are swept away with the morning. Now Costa fully understood, with the death of the Scorpion he understood. The Scorpion like he was a victim of natural selection, it was born the most despised of animals, as was Costa. It was a prisoner of circumstances. It wanted a better life, so much that it died for that. Perhaps Costa would have too.

But then what is life. . . .?

> '. . . it is a tale told by an idiot,
>   Full of sound and fury,
>   Signifying nothing . . .'

But it's all Costa's got.

PERVIN BATLIWALA   13

121

Awakening

I woke up slowly trying to recapture the threads of my dream, reaching out for the feeling of elation which had filled the night before. It was cold and the pale gold light feebly poked through the curtains. I stayed in bed until the last possible minute, cursing my mother and her little 'illnesses' which made these early morning trips to the doctor's frequent but in my opinion unnecessary. I grabbed the clock, ran for the bathroom, ran the water, washed my face, brushed my hair and galloped downstairs.

The house was unusually quiet, no sounds came from the lounge or kitchen and no early morning smells floated around. The light was pale and the whole house was bland, strangely neutral – almost – dead; I stood perfectly still, and the ticking of the clock was like thunder in my ears, by blood stormed through my body, every muscle throbbed and pulsed. I needed to scream, to shout, to run, but I could only stand, until my whole body sagged and my legs couldn't hold my weight. My thoughts blurred and sharpened, focussing on one thing then another, the air sickened and choked me, and I was aware only of myself and the knowledge that my mother was dead.

I raged against the word, the thought. I ran through the hall and up the stairs, without bothering to knock, I rushed into her bedroom shouting a greeting, then – I stopped. She was not beautiful or peaceful in death, her face was full, the skin loose now, flabby. Her mouth hung slightly open red and ugly, her stained eyelids against the white of her face looked slightly grotesque. I was shocked at my critical, cool feelings, yet I felt no horror, no sorrow, only a little fear. I wondered idly about my own future, my schooling, my new home, I acted as I should. I phoned the doctor, and knocked for my next door neighbour. I was not the 'brave girl' they thought, I did the obvious things and they required no effort.

The funeral (such an odd word, I often thought about it) meant nothing to me, the Browns and my relatives were very kind. I was very grateful to them, they fed me and amused me, and put me to bed. But I disappointed them, even though I 'bore up bravely', like all the best heroines. I was expected to be shocked into silence, then thrown into sorrowful torment, but I am not one of the best heroines. It amazed me, at times, the way they turned to God, my mother who had seen a church only twice in her adult live, and was not a particularly wonderful human being, had 'gone to a better place', would 'receive her just rewards', yet I couldn't think of her like that. I thought of her as dead, ceasing to exist, buried in the soil and rotting a little each day.

My Aunt Elizabeth and Uncle Harry looked after me very well, they fed me, clothed me and even loved me. Strangely I never missed my mother in the beginning, but as time passed I began to miss little things, which had never been important to me, tea which was too sweet, piles of paper-back books, which in my 'wisdom' I openly despised. Through my mother I could justify my existence by planning to change the world, by airing deep beliefs about God, mankind, myself, (and thinking myself very 'Hip'). In her I saw or thought I saw the mistakes of the older generation, 'the generation gap', the typical 'cabbage' of a woman, who thought about nothing and knew or cared about little but 'Coronation Street'. To her I thought myself superior, wiser, obliged to show her her mistakes, all judged by myself. It hurt me to realise that the Saint of my Aunt's dreams, and the villain of my own was a normal woman, not particularly beautiful, or talented, or religious and that she could never be remembered for what she was, and did, and thought, because nobody really knows what anyone else is, or what we ourselves are. It still hurts to miss her nagging about boyfriends, hours, new thoughts and ideas, and to realise that although we didn't have a startling relationship, we were too cautious, too afraid to say what we really thought, for that. I liked my mother and I never told her, she needed flowers when she was warm beside me, not cold in her shallow grave.

ANN MARIE CARLEN 15